WHICH WAY OUT

WHICH WAY OUT

Stories Based on the Experience of a Psychiatrist

by

C. P. Oberndorf M.D.

INTERNATIONAL UNIVERSITIES PRESS, INC.
New York   New York

In the course of many years of experience, every psychiatrist finds certain constant factors reappearing in the great variety of personalities and situations encountered. The characters and vicissitudes described in this book represent composites of those factors which have been most repetitive in nature during forty years of psychiatric work. None of the individual characters and none of the stories here recounted represent the characteristics or the experiences of any one individual ever known to the author. The names of all characters are fictitious excepting where reference is made to notable psychiatrists such as Freud, Kraepelin and Morton Prince. Any resemblances between any of the figures or names in the experiences in WHICH WAY OUT and any real person living or dead can therefore only be coincidental.

CONTENTS

INTRODUCTION

Interest in psychiatry and its individual, sociological and economic aspects has been on the increase since the beginning of the century. It has shown itself not only in the curricula of medical schools but in the daily press and in magazines ranging all the way from lurid serials to the most dignified literary periodicals. We may say without exaggeration that this spread of interest in psychiatric approaches to social questions was largely instigated by the psychoanalytic discoveries of Sigmund Freud. Psychoanalytic psychology has expanded enormously the clinical treatment of psychiatric cases outside of sanitaria and hospitals and has given to psychopathology a new theory and a system for the treatment of certain abnormalities of thought and action.

The mentally sick person sometimes regards himself as all bad or all good. Where the one is afflicted with an inferiority complex, the other may have delusions of grandeur. Only by taking an occasional inventory of his assets and liabilities is a person able to live a wholesome, constructive life. It is the psychiatrist's job to help bring this about.

To a psychiatrist there are no good people or bad people —he sees only variations in their strengths and weaknesses. For instance patience, forbearance and generosity are estimable qualities but when carried to extremes the policy of turning the other cheek may become abnormal humility. Also, courage, self-assertion and independence are commendable but when they are practiced with utter disregard for others they may be extremely destructive. Similarly, any exaggerated virtue becomes a handicap, such as trustfulness becoming gullibility or tidiness becoming an obsession. In

7

his sessions with the patient, however, the doctor may not speak too explicitly until the individual begins to understand his pathological defenses and discovers his own potentialities.

In the stories which take place in the office of the psychiatrist, psychoanalytic terms are often used. The description of the contact and conversation between the patient and physician does not reflect the technical procedure of an hour of psychoanalytic therapy. It would be impossible to convey completely and accurately to an outsider the psychic interplay in a routine psychoanalytic session even through a combined dictaphonic and cinematographic recording. Such a record would usually be extremely dull, with long silences, many trivialities and references which would be meaningless to a person not very familiar with the patient's entire background and would bear little resemblance to dramatized representations of the screen and stage. However, the psychological approach of the physician in the office-scenes of these stories is definitely that of a psychiatrist trained in the theory and methods of psychoanalysis.

Physicians have long been concerned with the question of the best methods for informing the general public of the procedures, achievements and aspirations of their science and art. Among the earlier and better-known attempts in literature are Dr. Anton Chekov's grim tales from his medical experience, and Dr. Conan Doyle's intriguing stories from practice, entitled *Around the Red Lamp*. Many authors, notably Goethe, Dostoevski, and Hawthorne have presented in fictional form the setting and dynamics of psychoanalysis, and recently an anthology of short stories by distinguished fiction writers illuminating "the neuroses of our time" has been assembled. Thus the layman and the non-specialist have been exposed to and sometimes have acquired a certain amount of information about the procedure.

In presenting these stories, it is my aim to illustrate some of the problems that repeatedly come to a psychiatrist's attention, using the career of Ben Ford to show the advances made in the field of psychiatric practice during the twentieth century. The episodes in the experience of the fictional Dr. Ford all have an authentic basis but are composite, having been derived from a number of actual private, clinic and hospital cases. The scenes are blended from memory of phases common to many persons having the same type of problem— suicidal ideas, feelings of rejection, conflict over infidelity and psychically influenced physical states.

Thus, the stories "Christmas Dinner" and "The Boarders" represent something more than incidents in the lives of men who from childhood had lived a hand-to-mouth existence. At the time they happened, physicians were gradually beginning to learn that, from an economic aspect, any form of illness is a drain not only on the individual but on all of society as well. Early in the twentieth century society was learning to appreciate realistically that it was economically unwise, medically unsound and socially unjust, to discharge from a hospital a penniless and homeless man or woman recently recovered from a severe illness or operation. Edward Devine's book, *Misery and Its Causes* (1903), focused public attention upon this fact. Examples of the vicious circle —illness causing poverty causing illness causing poverty— were particularly striking in patients from large municipal hospitals where the proportion of those permanently handicapped by chronic physical or mental deficiencies and poverty is particularly large. A few days after leaving, far too many of these patients had to return for further treatment because of relapses due to unavoidable early resumption of their overburdening work.

Tom Brennan in the first story may be regarded as typical of men who have been crippled by industrial accidents and are prematurely used up by the nature and the conditions of their life and work. To many such men alcohol offers a solacing anodyne for the hardships of existence. When they break physically and mentally, hospitals like Bellevue, in New York, become a temporary refuge, but when the acute condition has passed, complete convalescence is out of the question. The patient in "Christmas Dinner" went back to a city lodging house two days after an operation.

Nearly every illness—even a so-called trivial complaint—requires a new, if only transient, social adaptation on the part of the patient. Thus a permanently stiffened finger—certainly a minor affliction—demands a new mode of life, a lower position in the labor scale with less wage. Small wonder that the patient, Brennan, should have been tempted to capitalize on his handicap.

Mental illnesses are often of such long duration that the necessity for an altered social attitude affects almost equally the sufferer and members of his family. The impact of mental derangement upon others is almost sure to be sharper, more disagreeable and disrupting than any physical disease. This is true because in many instances the persons most intimately associated with the patient are involved in his abnormal antipathies and may become the objects of his hatred and abuse. For example, when a person suffers from a mental depression the immediate family may be greatly restricted in its usual social contacts and in cases of maniacal excitement they may be disturbed night and day by the patient's incessant overactivity. Furthermore, in many instances of mental aberration the parents or the brothers and sisters, the husband or the wife of the patient may feel in some measure responsible for its development. It then becomes the important though difficult function of the psychiatrist to safeguard the interests and health of the well in addition to caring for the sick. Discharge from a mental hospital is carefully deliberated by the staff to protect specific individuals and society as a whole from possible injury at the hand of a patient not completely recovered from delusional trends. Social workers now act as liaison agents between such patients and the hospitals.

It is being increasingly accepted that a psychiatric aspect complicates most situations which come to the attention of the social worker, a profession which was barely known at the beginning of this century. Only since then have hospitals come to recognize their position and obligations as social agencies and to regard the social aspects of illness as part of their medical organization and function. Forty years ago the main duties of the social worker were to investigate the economic status of "charity" patients and to assist with small funds those in need of financial help to tide them over the difficult days between discharge from the hospital and becoming self-supporting.

As more discerning social service developed, the connection between psychic maladjustment and poverty and continued ill health also grew more apparent. Better-trained personnel became more and more the investigators of social conditions, advisors and educators in healthful physical and mental living rather than agents rendering material aid or financial help. So it has come to pass that today many social workers regard these economic supportive activities as outside the scope of their attention, but men like those in "Christmas Dinner" and "The Boarders" resent it if they get nothing but advice no matter how valuable if the "old bread basket" is empty.

About the time of the incident described in "The Boarders" the scientific understanding of mental disease was hastened and advanced through the efforts of Dr. Adolph Meyer, then a young psychiatrist who had came to America from Switzerland. He had been actively engaged in the improvement of "insane asylums", as they were then called, in Illinois, Massachusetts, and New York State. The introduction of scientific methods such as laboratory tests, autopsies, experimentation with new drugs, and more thorough investigation of all of the facts pertaining to the patient's social and personal background, not only increased the recovery rate but attracted better-trained young physicians to the state hospital services and to the study of psychiatry. The effect of the new approach to mental disease through the dynamic and interpretative psychology which Freud had introduced a-broad under the name of psychoanalysis was at this time beginning to make itself felt in a few of the mental hospitals in America. It drew attention to the unconscious drives causing physical and mental disorder and also affecting the problems of family and community adjustment and social organization.

The appearance of disabling mental and physical symptoms against the expressed conscious wish of the individual was shown by Freud to occur frequently in cases called hysterical or generally neurotic. Freud urged the psychiatrist to look for the gain which the sufferer derives through his illness, a gain which is unconsciously more important than the distress and inconvenience of the symptoms. Thus, a young woman may complain very sincerely and bitterly that her particular symptom is ruining her life, is preventing all the social contacts which other girls enjoy, and is spoiling her chances of marriage. Actually she is suffering from a fear of leaving her home for an evening's pleasure or for a vacation in the country. Her confinement to the house is giving her something she unconsciously desires more than the social pleasures which she loses. Through the disabling symptom she may be protecting herself from the seduction that her dreams indicate she strongly desires; or she may be punishing her mother by insisting that the latter accompany her every time she does go out; or she may be obtaining the sympathy and attention of the entire family who otherwise might ignore her. Both "Gallant Father" and "The Christmas Card" deal with obscure pictures of disease resulting from such conflicts.

The feigning of insanity or stupidity to escape from a disagreeable or threatening situation is a device frequently met in the drama and in fiction. Most psychiatrists today lean to the belief that when an individual willfully simulates illness to gain his ends either in a civilian or a military situation, he does so because of a fundamental weakness or failure in adaptation. Hence, at the induction centers for selectees during the Second World War, if a man presented himself for examination with a host of bizarre complaints for which no physical basis could be established, the psychiatrists were likely to believe that his conscious and unconscious motives to avoid duty were sufficient reason to reject him as an individual who would stand up poorly under the discipline and rigors of army life or the stress of actual combat. Perhaps half of the discharges from the army for nervous illnesses were men who never had left this country or faced the enemy.

Painful and ugly incidents in family life, such as those portrayed in "The Bottle of Champagne", are likely to arouse deep bitterness and resentment, and when such feelings are entertained too long they may become the basis for pathological hatred toward the person considered responsible for them. The mechanism by which feelings of hostility and hatred toward others become reversed in a person's mind and interpreted as coming from those others was brilliantly described by Freud who called it "projection". Thus the evil thoughts by which a person considers himself abused are often originally his own, but he denies them as unworthy of himself. Subsequently he unconsciously allays his own feeling of unworthiness by claiming that he is not the sinner but the one sinned against. In the course of time such thoughts may become more or less systematized into permanent delusions of persecution.

It is still subject of controversy as to what extent a mental disturbance such as afflicted the girl in "The Bottle of

Champagne" or the imperious, reckless young woman in "Father's Baby Girl" is due to inherited constitution or to environment and specific attitudes in the training of the child—nature versus nurture. Often the two are interdependent. Innumerable cases have been observed in which the overprotection of parents has circumscribed to the point of isolation a child suffering from such a defect as club foot. On the other hand, instances come to mind, such as the infantile paralysis of the late President Franklin D. Roosevelt, in which the deformity acquired in middle life may have mobilized prodigious compensatory endeavors.

The "artistic" sets such as found in Munich are to be found in many large and small cities. Artists are persons possessed of the rare faculty of transforming emotion into other forms of expression, often without the medium of words. This gift in its highest form is rare. It is highly valued by those who have it in limited degree because it enables them to identify themselves readily and intensively with the honored masters in art fields. The artist usually develops his gift for expression at the expense of the desire to conform with the commonplace standards of his time. Such a lack of the desire to adapt himself, amounting at times to an incapacity, often makes him appear odd or unusual. It is this characteristic often found in the true artist—the inability and/or the unwillingness to conform—which so often attracts as to a refuge persons who are maladjusted and possess only a meager capacity for converting their emotional reactions into any type of artistic expression. They mingle with groups known as artists hoping that their inadequacies, of which they are aware, will be considered "artistic"—condoned as something exceptional. They hope thereby to escape the criticism which society metes out to the average person who deviates too far from custom and regulation.

The advent of psychoanalysis and its application to the neuroses brought about a new era in the treatment of mental illness because it provided the physician with a method which enabled him to help many patients previously sent to private sanitaria or public hospitals. To be sure, psychoanalysis is a slow and tedious procedure, often uncertain in its final beneficial results and requiring sessions of an hour between the physician and the patient. It is not infrequent for such treatments to continue five times a week for two years or more. One of the greatest obstacles to altering the attitudes of patients through psychoanalysis is the tenacity with which they cling to their long-established habits of thought, patterns that have engendered the distorted view of actualities as well as of the ethical and moral problems so often involved in the neuroses. Both consciously and unconsciously the patient opposes and rejects the physician's efforts to bring about a change. The physician instead of fighting back remains passive or repeats the disquieting question, "And what comes to your mind?" or says: "Let's consider this aspect of the situation which you yourself brought up but are now avoiding."

In psychoanalysis the unconscious opposition of the patient is called resistance. One of the most common forms of resistance is the evasion of the situation or topic which the patient most fears and the substitution of digressions into less threatening though more immediate worries. It may be surprising to the average person but it is nevertheless true that most neurotics, like those in "The Will" and "The Gun", notwithstanding their acute sufferings and the cost and tedium of analytic therapy, seek to defer making any fundamental changes whatsoever, preferring rather to discuss over and over again their woes and dilemmas. In short, they more or less deliberately halt the progress of the cure. Physicians sometimes attempt to disrupt this tendency toward stagnation by requesting the patient to undertake some step which he fears. This is called active therapy. Such active therapy is not introduced with the idea that by going through with the act the patient will overcome his fears, but that the emotional reactions he experiences at the time will bring out impressive reactions which may furnish clues to the unknown (unconscious) origins of his phobias.

The symptom in the case of "The Will"—namely, falling asleep during the analytic treatment hour—is, to be sure, a rare but nevertheless an extremely effective means of postponing contemplation of distressing topics or decisions. It removes the patient from the dangers and demands of reality and allows actual experiences to become remote and dim. This tendency to allow "things to go by the board" may temporarily make painful situations less acute, but if it is adopted as a design for living it will eventually deprive the individual of all emotional feeling, the joys and thrills and interests of life, as the price he must pay for the selfish prudence which evades all pain.

That the theme of suicide should occur so prominently in three stories—"The Will", "The Visitor", and "The Gun"—was not premeditated. The fact is that the psychiatrist deals with the grim aspects of life and the idea of suicide is frequently met in many forms of mental illness but particularly in depressions, some neuroses, and occasionally in schizophrenia. The thought of death as a way out of one's difficulties may appear even in the early years of childhood and is found with almost every one who is psychoanalyzed. The wish to die—and its converse the wish to kill—comes to many people at some time in their lives, but usually it is only a fleeting thought from which they rebound immediately, leaving no deep effect on their general attitude. However, when persons find themselves repeatedly in distressing predicaments for which they consider themselves responsible, the thought of death may increase in frequency and intensity.

The desire to die and also to kill, or the persistent thought to kill oneself, is usually nourished by a feeling of guilt concerning the blame for the person's distress. This guilt in turn is often based upon a suppressed or secret hatred of other people—usually those to whom the person would like to feel near and dear—parents, siblings, children—and the hostility may increase to the point where he desires to murder those whom he feels he should venerate or protect.

The child's idea of retaliating against a grownup who denies him the love he craves or who opposes him too harshly is expressed in the phrase, "You'll be sorry when I'm dead". Adults who harbor violent impulses against close friends or relatives often cannot quite justify the fact to themselves, so they suppress their impulses, either through conscious fear of the possible consequences or because of an unconscious guilt which is continuously operative. Occasionally impulses to violence cannot be controlled indefinitely in the face of repeated rejection at the hands of desired, admired or envied persons, so that, finally, instead of retaining the original form of a force seeking to attack others, the embittered person turns these impulses for destruction against his own body. It is just such an intrapsychic situation which made a patient who was contemplating suicide remark to me, "No one ever voluntarily commits suicide, he is driven to it".

This comment might well apply to the tragic end of the aging spinster in "The Visitor" who felt forced to take her own life because of continued failure to secure the love and attention of her family, augmented, of course, by the feeling of guilt concerning her inability to escape from homosexual urges. A similar mechanism is apparent in the Professor's impulse for suicide in "The Gun". His own need to control the direction of his aggressive impulses compelled him to reject the Negro's proposal to put him out of this life. One might infer, too, that the suicide of the father of the patient in "The Will" was determined by the primal hostility which the old man felt for his little son at birth

as well as by the failure of his own subsequent attempts to
make amends for it, culminating when the son finally condemned him.

The choice of the method of suicide also has its unconscious motivations. In general the method is either mild,
as by inhaling gas or taking an overdose of a sedative drug,
or violent, as by shooting or hanging. The first type, very
broadly speaking, is symbolically feminine, the latter a
masculine mode of self-destruction. A person not fully determined on suicide may cling to the idea that none but his
own method of self-destruction would satisfy him as in the
case of the Professor who would use only the gun. Such a
person usually selects some form which is particularly difficult for him to carry out—when a feminine man resolves
that only shooting himself would satisfy him as his final
act.

In clinical practice frequent threats of suicide should
never be ignored or neglected by the physician. The expression of suicidal ideas must be interpreted as a plea on
the part of the patient for help. It represents his vacillation between a desire to relinquish his hostility against the
world or turn it against himself. So the physician confronted
with these threats of suicide tries to bring into the open the
motives which impel the patient to admit defeat in life's
unavoidable conflicts by committing suicide—an act which
he may come to recognize as an empty and often unjustifi-
able revenge and retaliation either against someone toward
whom he is unwarrantly embittered or against a generally
unappreciative world. Through decreasing the patient's unconscious hostility, whatever its target may be, the physician
seeks to transform the destructive impulses into constructive
and productive ones, thereby renewing the patient's interest
in living and in life. Even when the patient cannot be induced to relinquish completely his murderous longings, discussion and interpretation may weaken them sufficiently so

that he becomes resigned to continue living with a more tolerant view of the denials to which he felt he had been subjected.

A frequent external situation which tends to induce neurotic illness and accentuate the difficulties in marital adaptation is the waning of interest and the neglect of one member of a couple by the other. Often, as in the story of "The Busy Doctor", it is due to overinvestment of time and energy in work, to the exclusion of interest in those who should be nearest the individual. It occurs not only among professional men and business executives but also among those in lowlier positions. I recall one instance of a keeper of a small delicatessen store whose fervent devotion to his hams, potato-salad and pickles led to the frequent infidelity of his wife which in turn caused her to lapse into a grave depression.

Often in such cases the excessive interest in work is the result of the individual's inability to invest his love in living objects. Usually this is due to an extraordinary self-love from which he cannot free himself and which makes him feel blameworthy when he is unable to enter wholeheartedly into a love relationship with the opposite sex. At other times it may be caused by unconscious homosexual attachments which prevent a full and deep interest in the husband or wife, as the case may be. The rest of the family, of course, is entirely unaware of the causes of the disinterest of the particular member in their hopes and ambitions. The children in such cases may suffer under a neglect of which they gradually become aware through comparison of the standards in their own homes with those of the families of their friends.

Not infrequently the attitude of indifference on the part of the husband or wife in the role of father or mother may end in an abrupt tragedy, such as when one of the children disappears from home, or has an inappropriate love episode, which is unconsciously motivated by a desire to disgrace the parent, or in the case of an adult, to humiliate the offending mate. Another outcome of overinvestment in work may be an emotional awakening after many years to realization that life is barren, that work alone no longer satisfies; or, as in the case of "The Busy Doctor", a suddenly found emotional maturity may seek satisfaction in the blending of a normal human attachment with professional ambition.

On the other hand, as in the sordid little drama, "Through Forever", mutual guilt or perverse indulgence may tend to bind two people in a marital or illegitimate relationship not entirely satisfactory to either one. Counter-accusations allow each to project his guilt upon the other, so that the bickering couple at the same time relieve themselves and punish each other. In such cases the unconscious satisfaction in continuing the situation may be sufficiently strong to prevent any attempt on the part of the psychiatrist to bring about a less irritating and a more healthy form of adaptation between the two persons.

The central problem in both "Father's Baby Girl" and "Gallant Father" is that of incest, an actuality in the first story, but an unconscious urge in the second. Freud found that such unconscious incestuous attachments exert an important influence in the development of neurotic manifestations and in the determination of adult love life. He described it as the Oedipus complex adopting the term from the theme of the old Greek tragedy, Oedipus Rex.

In practically every psychoanalysis, no matter for what symptom or syndrome it is undertaken, this incestuous longing for the parent of the opposite sex and the manner in which it is resolved is thoroughly investigated. An unconscious attachment to a father or a mother may lead to a precipitate flight from the situation into sexuality with a man or woman of distinctly lower station, or at times the individual may protect himself or herself through assuming the characteristics of the unconsciously loved parent. In psychoanalytic theory the conflict caused by the failure to resolve the Oedipus attachment in the course of normal maturation is held responsible for much deviation in social conduct as well as for symptoms which seem physical. Uncertainties of conduct are portrayed in the errant daughter in "Father's Baby Girl"; characteristic physical symptoms of the rejection of motherhood occur to the diffident young wife in "Gallant Father".

Today in America it is relatively seldom that mentally ill patients develop such manifest physical symptoms as hysterical blindness or the inability to walk or talk, as the chief expression of their illness, while their physical and emotional behavior remains otherwise well within average, normal limits. However, such symptoms are still seen quite frequently among simple-minded people and sometimes among children. Generally speaking, these symptoms disappear more quickly than the compulsion neuroses or the anxiety states which are prevalent among more intelligent and cultured individuals.

The episode of quick recovery in "The Christmas Card" is based upon an actual case: this patient had been in bed for years unable to walk but a "miraculous" cure was achieved very largely because external circumstances had interrupted the unconscious gain which the patient had been deriving from her illness. Some elements included in this story were operative in another patient who responded similarly to brief psychotherapeutic treatment. The incapacitating physical symptom (vomiting) disappeared quickly and was succeeded by a deep and permanent religious conversion. In both instances prolonged treatment was unnecessary for an adequate adjustment to life's demands, and the patients—both women—remained well over the many years I was able to follow them.

A word may also be said about the influence of fantasy-life

on the reactions of the individual and in the production of guilt feelings. The question may well be raised whether in "The Christmas Card" the patient's guilt would have been greater or less had she actually committed adultery with the man who served as her phantom lover. In a general way it is easier for the analyst to deal with actual situations than with fantasy, for in the former the patient cannot evade completely the impact of reality. When, however, the situation exists only in the imagination or concerns someone who has passed away, the representation of it can be distorted to fit the patient's own unconscious yearnings. One of my patients, aged sixty, who had continued to entertain a very strong attachment to a brother who had died at fourteen when she herself was only eight, remarked to me: "The only way to stay young is to die young. My brother Robert is still the handsome lad of fourteen. I have never thought how he would be when he grew up." I suggested that now he would be about sixty-six, possibly with a paunch and a bald head. "I shudder to think of it", responded the old lady.

A number of "inferiorities" which trouble patients in one form or another have also been intentionally introduced into the synthesized picture of "The Christmas Card". These factors, such as insanity in the family or membership in an inferior social, religious or economic group, are often overemphasized by patients as prominent causes of their conflicts and disabilities. Usually the harmful and disturbing influence of these "causes" is far from essential or fundamental but displaced from situations or practices of which the person is far more ashamed.

Neuroses occur in persons who are socially most advantageously situated as well as in those who may be handicapped by belonging to a minority group in respect to race, creed, or color. It can be discovered on deeper investigation that the complaints based on these obvious reasons mask repressed personal attachments and conflicts similar to those which give rise to anxieties and compulsions in members of the most favorably placed classes.

The hope in the fight against mental illness lies not only in its cure but far more in its prevention. The prophylactic approach is now being fostered by child guidance clinics, school psychiatrists, psychiatric clinics and wards in general hospitals, and by the care of mental disturbances in adult life before they have become too severe or have reached the stage where residence in a closed mental institution is desirable. That the task appears at times to be overwhelming has not deterred the efforts of physicians and educators and sociologists, but rather has acted in recent years as an incentive to vastly increased activity on their part which also receives cooperation from the general public. The outlook for decrease is hopeful although it is impossible to say whether in the future the greatest contributions to cure and prevention will come from psychology, physiology, biology or some still undiscovered approach.

I

CHRISTMAS DINNER

Bellevue, the municipal hospital of New York, is an imposing group of buildings covering a quarter of a square mile fronting on Manhattan Island's East River, all completely planned before a steam shovel gouged the earth for the foundation of the first unit. At the turn of the century it consisted of a drab main building with thick grey stone walls, over fifty years old. To this central structure irregular grey wings had been added from time to time and around it a variety of brick pavilions and long, single-storied frame houses spread out irregularly.

But medical students of that time looked eagerly and hopefully to internships in this somber hospital, for the low outlying buildings housed types of patients not admitted to other general hospitals—alcoholics, men and women muttering and screaming in their delirium; the insane, from whom doctors could learn much of human strivings and failures; the tubercular, the pale, thin victims of the "great white plague", which medicine had only recently learned was an infection; erysipelas which spread its deadly scarlet scourge from patient to patient like a forest fire.

Competition for positions on Bellevue's house staff was keen and it was a surprise to Benjamin Ford, about twenty-four years old, a senior at the Cornell Medical School, when he learned that he had been selected.

"Well, Benny, you made Bellevue—right up at the top of the list," exclaimed one of his fellow students, "how did you do it? Starting service in July to boot. Must have been a fluke."

24

The high-ceilinged cheerless hall of Bellevue's ancient main building seemed gloomier than usual on that dark afternoon of the twenty-third of December, and the dim lights which had just been lit did little to dispel the gloom. Two young physicians in white duck suits stood there talking.

"You're holding up the service this afternoon from four to eight, Benny," said the taller and older of the two, "and if any one wants me remember that you've telephoned all over the Hospital for Dr. Nasmyth and have not been able to locate him anywhere. Savvy, Dr. Ford?"

"Yes, and me just a junior, the kid of your staff. How can you trust me to replace you for so long in your exalted job?" replied the other, a slim, earnest-looking young man with thick, straight brown hair carefully parted down the middle.

"Entirely irrelevant," continued Nasmyth with a twinkle. "It will be of great help as well as an honor for you to officiate as a real surgeon before you start on your downward career of peddling pills and vile tasting tonics on the medical wards. The service is light just now and there won't be much doing. I'm off on a most important operation."

"Which one of the queens are you operating on now, Smitty? I'll bet it's that new red-headed junior nurse, the nifty one on Ward 12 with the sky-high pompadour and Gibson-girl walk."

"Young man, don't be impertinent. Remember while we're in this building you're just a plain junior addressing his superior, the house-surgeon! Well, my lad, I'm off," said Nasmyth.

Ford watched him affectionately as he made off for the afternoon and its "important operation". Smitty—as everyone about the hospital called him, from stretcher-carrier to head nurse—was a heart-breaker but he was also a young man of great talent and distinction among the group of clever young doctors on the staff of the great city hospital. He would be leaving soon—right after Christmas—having come to the end of his highly successful six months' service as house-surgeon. Everyone at Bellevue would miss Smitty, and not least Benny Ford, because of their association which had ripened into friendship.

In a mood more suitable for reverie than for work, Ford went to the junior doctors' dormitory to wait for a possible summons. There, sprawled in a Morris chair, he surveyed the huge, bare-walled, loft-like room, only half aware of its ugliness and disorder. Four iron cots and four cheap oak dressers took up most of the space. On the old, shabby chairs were strewn ties, white duck coats and underwear, and under the beds lay scattered an assemblage of shoes, black, tan, white. Outside a raging wintry storm rattled the loose panes in two wide, ceiling-high windows. A cold dampness which hung over the East River penetrated the stuffy air of the room but the steam radiators hissed comfortably. And Ford was content. All his immediate medical duties had been finished; no emergency case, such as a crushed skull, a broken leg, or a bad burn had turned up. Nasmyth would be back at eight. He felt entitled to dawdle there, lounging in his crumpled white suit and somewhat elated, too, at the idea of being in charge of surgery—if only for the moment. He was glad to be a part of Bellevue's comfortable informality, satisfying realism and unpretentious, unassuming humanism—felt lucky to be there.

It was the patient, as well as his disease, who interested Ford and because of that predilection he had been a tag-ender at the Medical School during his first years. He thought the endless enumerations of the anatomical studies, the perpetual peering through microscopes at dead tissues, the recording of chemical reactions, the memorizing of countless, obsolete drugs and their dosages boring and incomprehensible. In old Bellevue he had found all that he had envisaged when he chose medicine as a career. Here he discovered some of the visions of his adolescence, the modern replicas of the benevolent physician of Balzac's *Country Doctor*, and comforting old Doctor Lavendar of Margaret Deland's *Old Chester Tales*, and the more modern, psychologically inclined Doctor Eskridge in the *Constance Trescot* of S. Weir Mitchell, himself a noted neurologist.

Young Ford, something of a dreamer, had pictured himself as one who would be in a position to help ease the ills of people, mental as well as physical. Thank heaven, the dull tasks of theorizing and memorizing of medical school days were over. Now, in Bellevue he was at last coming in real contact with humanity. Here, whatever might interest the man of medicine, the healer or the scientist, was sure to present itself. Through the weathered gates of this hospital passed an endless line of those crippled in body and spirit. Into its courtyard horse-drawn ambulances never ceased clanging with their cargo of maimed and suffering people. Yes, he was fortunate to be here.

He was roused from his reverie when Jimmy, the orderly with the pinched white face and the sharp red nose, limped in with a slip notifying the house-surgeon of an admission to the ward. It read: Time—4:30 P.M.; Name—Tom Brennan; Diagnosis—for operation.

The words "for operation" put Ford at once on the alert. Could it be a ruptured appendix, peritonitis, or something equally urgent which needed immediate attention? On the other hand it might be just a trifling affair. In any case it called for a visit to the surgical ward promptly.

There he found a derelict—a thin, middle-aged man in a threadbare suit, shivering disconsolately on a chair. He still clutched at the collar of his coat about his neck, so chilled had he been by the cold mist outside. His worn, rough, leaky shoes were wet with slush. A collarless shirt showed a gaunt neck with a large, bony Adam's apple. The man looked frozen, but not seriously ill, as he sat there thawing out, with bleary eyes staring vacantly into space. Dr. Ford had already come to recognize his type—city bum or country hobo—the man who had never had much of a chance in life.

There were many—far too many—of them who, poorly equipped from birth, reared in city tenements or small town slums, grew up without direction. Then they left school at about twelve for the first job offered them, began wandering, drinking too hard when they could as their only means of escape from their poverty and unhappiness. They aged too quickly so that by the time they had reached forty they were old, and often crippled in some part of the body—chronically handicapped because of a badly-knit broken leg, or because of swollen, beer-soaked livers which made their ankles swell, or because of hard arteries in their brain which made them dizzy when they climbed or bent.

The desolate man, as Dr. Ford saw him, certainly did not present anything medically exciting.

"What's the matter, Brennan?" he asked, glancing down at the admission slip to recapture the name.

The man's mind seemed to be as sluggish as his frozen body, thawing out slowly like the slush which was beginning to turn into little puddles on the floor around the wet soles of his shoes. It took Tom Brennan a few minutes to gather his thoughts before they could flow into action and words. At last he raised his right hand shakily and showed a stiff, shrivelled index finger still purple with cold.

"It's dis finger, Doc. I want to have it orf. I wuz here in Bellevue four or five years ago—dis finger and my arm wuz all swelled up—fever blood-poisoning. De doctors didn't know if dey could save me, but dey did—all but dis finger. When dey sent me out after a while de big soigin says to me: 'My man, I don't know if dat finger is wurt' more to you orf or on. Try it dis way fer a while, we can always take orf but we can't put back on'."

Dr. Ford examined the almost rigid finger which he could bend forward just a bit where it joined the hand. The skin had become taut over the bone. The tendons and muscles had withered from lack of use. It stood out like a stripped, dead branch of an elm tree which has been deprived of sunlight by other grotesquely twisting branches growing from the same trunk.

"How did it happen?" asked Ford.

"I got it from er scratch, openin' a tin can at the Palace Restaurant right here down on Foist Avenue. I like woikin' in restaurants when I can—but it's awful tough for a job dis winter."

Of course, disuse and age were continually decreasing the value of the rod-like finger until at times it must have been an impediment to work rather than an aid. After a moment's reflection, Ford decided that the original surgeon's judgment years ago had probably been for the best. So he said to the sodden figure before him:

"I think you had better keep that finger for a while longer. I'll have you sent out now."

Ford pronounced this decision with some reluctance and a twinge of conscience. The weather outside was cruelly bitter for one as scantily clad as the spare, harried man sitting before him. Even the walk to the city lodging house a few blocks away would be a hardship. Ford felt he had little choice, however. The beds in the ward were all filled with sick, helpless men; some of the convalescents would be obliged to sleep on box springs on the floor that very night. What justification could he find for keeping a man with so trivial a complaint in the hospital?

"Oh, no, Doc! I want dat finger orf. When it's cold like dis I jus' can't stand de pain. It's got to come orf now," protested the worried man with an alarmed, despairing glance at the gale-swept street.

This was an unusual situation. When so many patients needed to be reassured and coaxed into an operation, here was a man actually pleading for one. Of course, Ford reflected, it was not his own finger but the man's and he had been living with it for years, knew its advantages and drawbacks. Nevertheless, Ford was puzzled. He wondered what might be the motives behind the patient's insistence, at the same time fleetingly conscious that his interest lay more in the patient himself than in his complaint.

On the other hand, it would be a neat little operation for Smitty before he finished his service and Ford was almost sure Dr. Hartley, the Visiting Surgeon, would turn the amputation over to him. Ford knew that the eminent Hartley regarded Nasmyth with great favor and would stand by at the table, offering Smitty only a suggestion now and then from his own rich experience.

"All right, you can stay. We'll do the operation tomorrow."

A fleeting look of curious hopelessness came over the face of the possessor of the stump. Then he brightened a bit as he assented with an, "All right, Doc".

As Ford turned to leave the ward, Brennan slowly shuffled off towards the room where he could remove his crumpled, wet clothes, take the required warm shower, receive clean, faded, pink-striped, cotton-flannel pajamas, and be ready in time for the evening meal which ambulatory patients ate in a little room off the ward pantry.

An hour later he had made himself at home, helping the tired nurses with a skill and affability which astonished them. He was apparently familiar with all the hospital routine. Had not this stump of a finger in past years gained him admittance to various hospitals whenever he was up against it? As the night nurses arrived at seven o'clock, little Miss

Evans nodded in Tom's direction and winked at her successor, "he's a God-send".

When Dr. Ford made evening rounds, Brennan lay curled up on a hospital cot, his empty grey eyes staring ahead, the stubble of his chin looking dirtier and more disorderly against the whiteness of the pillow-case. Ford passed him by with a "How are you?" and in an aside to the nurse ordered the regular diet and cathartic pills prescribed for all new patients.

Behind Brennan's vacant look moved his befuddled mind, confronted by a problem which seemed hopelessly beyond its capacity to solve. He had faced the problem often before —this threat of an operation which would separate him from his meal ticket, deprive him of the occasional periods of refuge he was in the habit of finding in hospitals. That stump of a finger was, after all, very valuable to him. It was, in fact, his fortune. Now, the doctor had scheduled its removal for the following day. Desperately he wanted now to avoid that operation, to escape the imminent danger of that loss.

A shadowy premonition had worried him as he had trudged up through the slush of First Avenue that afternoon with just four cents in the greasy, left hand pocket of his pants. His worn shoes were stiff from the cold; his feet numb from lack of blood, faltered. His mind, always vague, became more confused than ever. The puckered mucus lining of his empty stomach and the lean marrow of his brittle bones began making a decision for him as his thinking ceased. The pathways of action and thought were reversed. The organs of the body automatically took over control with an autocratic authority. They would preserve themselves at all costs without waiting for orders from the mind.

Something had to be done right away. His aching feet and the thin marrow of his bones determined that Bellevue was nearest. "Try Bellevue again", urged the gnawing stomach. The remnant of his thinking self protested feebly and sought hazily to resist the usurpation of its functions by rebellious guts and flagging muscles. The mind sensed rather than reasoned that Bellevue, with its business-like system, its bustle, its familiarity with men like him, was fraught with danger. Bellevue was accustomed to dealing quickly with emergencies, large ones as well as small. Bellevue was unpredictable—sometimes lax and slack, but at others despotic as Brennan had discovered when he had first been admitted there for this very amputation. On that occasion he had delayed coming to a decision so long that his mind had been able to give forceful orders only at the last minute— while the orderly was wheeling him to the operating room. Then Brennan had struck out with his fists; there had been a brief struggle during which the orderly had jolted him on the jaw. Then he had been hustled out of the hospital— back to security, the precarious security of a lasting, if periodic, ticket for admission to the shelter and food of a hospital.

Yes, Brennan thought, the day had been a fortunate one when the great surgeon had decided in favor of conservatism in regard to the scarred finger. During his convalescence from the original infection he had become familiar with ward routine and had discovered the privileges which the nurses allow to willing up-patients. He had seen many a helpful patient's discharge postponed for days—strictly against regulations—because he assisted cheerfully with disagreeable hospital chores. His bad finger had become his good-luck piece. He called it his free meal ticket. It assured him admission to almost any hospital, usually for two or three days—sometimes longer—until the date set for operation. That catastrophe he had always previously been able to evade . . .

Promptly at eight o'clock that evening Smitty, punctilious

and reliable, poked his head into the dormitory where the four juniors snatched sleep between endless telephone calls and notes from their senior physicians.

"Anything new, Benny?"

"Yes, a little operation for your last day. Amputation of the stump of a forefinger—one of those hopeless old fellows of forty-five came in and almost demanded the operation. I've scheduled it as the final case tomorrow—I know you'll do something artistic."

The day before Christmas Tom Brennan awoke at six o'clock from a sound sleep, yawned, rolled his tongue in his mouth, smacked his lips in the hunger that had awakened him. He felt refreshed in spirit. It took a few moments to realize where he was and to appraise once more the threat in his present situation. With habitual indolence he postponed making a decision. His mind was dominated by thoughts of the ward pantry, that unfailing source of solace, and of the prerogative it gave him of large portions and the choicest morsels of food. He gravitated there and busied himself. And by the time the surgeons appeared on morning rounds, he had established himself firmly in the affections of the stunted old woman who served as the ward helper.

At a little after ten the staff straggled in, a small cavalcade of crisp-looking nurses in blue and white striped uniforms, and young fellows in white headed by the self-confident Smitty. As they approached Tom's bed in their progress around the ward, he braced himself for the ordeal, made a decision and took the initiative.

"Doc, dis finger aint' no good to me."

"And you think that you want it off," finished the young surgeon, examining it. Then, to Tom's dismay after a quick but thorough examination, the surgeon pronounced his judgment.

"You had better keep it where it belongs. An operation

is not absolutely necessary. I'll send you out this morning."

"Now, Doc, I wuz down to de Beekman Street 'orspital and de big soigin dere said dis finger better come orf. It won't be no big opyration. I come here because I heerd dat Bellevue wuz de best doctors."

A delicate situation confronted the young surgeon. He had acquired the surgeon's point of view—the surgeon's urge to test his skill, the surgeon's pride in confronting a technical challenge. Without doubt the great Hartley would not only recommend the radical approach—he would disapprove of conservatism which he would say was based on lack of confidence. Smitty's experience in amputations had been limited. He wavered only a moment.

"Well," he murmured, "it's your finger. I don't know that the operation actually needs to be done, but . . ."

"Yes, Doc, I'm goin' ter have it orf."

"Then, we'll give you ether this afternoon. The usual pre-operative precautions about food, Miss Beverly."

With this ultimatum the little group passed on to the next bed.

Tom Brennan's chin fell into his knotted hand. Ether! He knew ether only too well—its stifling, sweetish odor, the struggling and straining in going under, the abominable nausea, the retching and groaning, then the interminable vomiting and depression on coming out. He had watched enough patients recovering from ether to have decided that he would never voluntarily submit to taking it. To Tom's knowledge of hospital routine it also meant one other thing —no dinner that day, or the next.

Later, he started up several times to tell the nurse that he had changed his mind and had decided to leave. But he had been in similar predicaments before. The operation might be postponed by the doctors, as it had been once before in another hospital when a difficult emergency operation had taken precedence and given him several days' grace. They might let him stay. They might forget—a vague something might happen to keep him at Bellevue over Christmas. He concluded to wait until operation time to decide.

The ward was beginning to put on its holiday dress. Long, slim festoons of evergreens swung from the centre of the ceiling to the corners of the room. Between the beds the red and dark green of holly wreaths relieved the monotony of the faded nile green walls. The windows, too, were draped in cedar and holly. Well concealed over the archway to an alcove holding medicine cabinets, a spray of mistletoe had been hung by a nurse.

Tom Brennan could not resist joining with the convalescents in helping with the decoration of the ward though his impending ordeal weighed heavily upon him. Outside, the white storm continued blowing and whirling. Now and then chilling blasts came through a crack at the top of a window frame. He dreaded to leave the snug room but he appreciated that if he delayed until the afternoon the operation might become unavoidable. Suddenly the terrifying thought overwhelmed him—if he submitted to the operation, the nausea of the ether would prevent him from eating Christmas dinner the next day. Oh, no! He really could not submit to such a sacrifice, a sacrifice which entailed not only being deprived of eventual profit from this precious stump of a finger, but the immediate sacrifice of a festive meal as well. He must act quickly!

A porter came through carrying into the kitchen a basket of shining red apples and pungent oranges. A messenger boy followed him with eight tempting mince pies, large ones—a gift of the Ladies' Auxiliary. Convalescents from operations have lusty appetites . . . A hurried nurse told the boy to leave them on a table in the middle of the room. Then the old woman from the kitchen hobbled through with an open basket heavy with celery, nuts and raisins, and a fourteen-pound turkey already roasted golden brown.

Time passed unnoted.

"Brennan, you'd better get into bed now. We've got to prepare you for the operation," called a nurse.

Mechanically he obeyed. Still unable to decide upon what action to take, he remained in bed looking dismally at his long-treasured deformity. Indifferent and vague in his vacillation, he watched the clock as the minutes passed. The nurses in white gowns were scurrying in and out of a small operating room just off the ward preparing for the afternoon's work.

"Well, dere ain't goin' ter be no opyration," murmured Tom softly and definitely to himself.

At four o'clock Dr. Ford appeared before Tom, wheeling a white enamelled surgical truck. On it lay a clean gauze mask. Several cans of ether seemed to be popping out of each pocket in his coat.

"Have you any false teeth, chewing gum or tobacco in your mouth?" he asked as a matter of routine.

Brennan's resolve was strong now. "I ain't goin' ter take no dope," he said with emphasis. "Where's de soigin? I got er bad heart an' I can't take no dope."

Ford placed his stethoscope here and there over the chest and finding the heart action steady and strong he attempted to reassure the man. It availed nothing. Brennan would listen to no argument.

Finally Smitty in a long white gown and skull cap came out of the operating room, his face flushed with irritation and annoyance at the delay. Hartley had sarcastically been inquiring whether the patient had arrived yet from Florida. Smitty avoided touching anything with his rubber-gloved hands, holding them stiffly in the air.

"What's the trouble in getting this man under, Benny?" he asked.

"Doc, I got er bad heart an' I can't take no dope," broke in Brennan.

"Oh, ether will do your heart good—it's a stimulant for the heart—better than whisky, and you know how good that is! Either you will have the operation now, or you can put on your clothes."

From his bed Tom Brennan could see the snow, driven furiously across the East River, swishing against the windows. From the ward pantry floated in the aroma of cooking food and with it thoughts of the Christmas turkey about which the men in the ward had been joking all day. The whiff of hot beef tea which an orderly was distributing among the patients from bed to bed agonized him and made him waver. His nostrils and salivary glands now assumed control. It went through his sluggish mind that he could get along very well without the finger, but of what good were turkey or mince pies to a man coming out of ether?

"You've only a minute to decide," interrupted the cold voice of the surgeon, Dr. Nasmyth. He had no inkling as to the reasons for the patient's vacillation.

"Doc, I want de opyration, but dat ether—ain't dere any way—jes' wait er day—maybe my heart might be better tomorrer."

"Afraid of ether, are you? Well, we'll do it under local."

"What's dat, Doc," inquired Tom, hopefully, fearfully.

"Local anesthesia—a new method—not so new either. By just sticking you with a needle once or twice, we can put in a medicine all around the finger and you won't feel it —hardly at all."

"Can't you wait until tomorrer?" pleaded Tom. "I'll tink about it until then."

"We rest on Christmas Day. Now—or not in Bellevue. Quick, now, make up your mind."

Smitty's tone sounded a bit pitiless to Ford, but surgeons are likely to acquire that manner when in action. Their very impersonality, their coldness, is an important element in their skill. Then, for the first time, it dawned upon young Ford's mind that the whistling wind outside might be the deciding factor in the afflicted man's hesitation.

A Christmas tree had just been placed in a corner of the ward laden with pink and white candy canes, glistening fruits, trinkets and tinsel, paper angels and candles. The mince pies still lay piled upon the table, tantalizingly in full view.

"How long will I have ter stay after de opyration?"

"Oh, only a day or two. We can't wait forever."

"Dere won't be no ether, an' it won't hoit?"

"Very little."

Tom glanced tenderly at the precious finger. Then he looked out at the cold darkness gathering outside and let his eyes wander around the festive ward. A blast of wind again howled against the panes of the loose windows. The whistling wind whispered unseen, unheard, in conspiracy with the latent ache in the lean bone marrow. The incredible, invisible conference automatically arrived at a conclusion.

"Is it wurt' it?" the confused, defeated mind pondered.

"Last call for operation in the operating room!"

The pungent odors from the kitchen off the ward again reached Tom's nostrils, his hollow stomach, and penetrated to the void of fat in the marrow.

"I guess—dat—finger—got ter come—orf."

On Christmas Day a semblance of the Christmas spirit crept into the grim room of suffering. Only the most necessary treatments had been ordered so that an air of relative calm and peace pervaded the ward. A close observer might have noticed that the few doctors on duty made frequent visits with one of the nurses to inspect the medicine cabinets standing beyond the alcove where the concealed mistletoe hung. The day supervisor ignored the sprig although she knew it had been there every Christmas Day since she had been a shy probationer in that very ward twenty years ago.

At noontime Ford sauntered into the ward. He sat at the nurses' desk watching the patients as they began to eat Christmas dinner. There were other things which were waiting for him to do yet he could not resist staying on. There was an irresistible appeal in the scene, differing so greatly from his own boyhood background. He had not been at Bellevue long enough to have become familiar with the people he was seeing there. This was his first hospital Christmas dinner.

Today an unusual atmosphere of kindliness filled the drab old ward and he knew it was due to the nurses. They were all there, though a glance at the clock told him that it was long past the hour when several of them should have gone off duty for their own holiday. He watched their capable hurry to pass out the trays while the food was still hot, yet still finding time in an unhurried way for a few cheery words and an occasional bit of extra attention for each patient. As he had watched these nurses day by day carry on a seemingly never-ending load of work, he had thought they were indifferent, even calloused, to what went on around them. Now it had come to him that in the huge hospital's backwash of human flotsam and their misery, these girls skillfully did their tasks, wasting no time in fruitless sentimentality. They knew they could change nothing in the mistakes and injustices of society but they could help its victims a bit. So they did their best always.

The younger men, with hope ahead of them, even one whose leg had been amputated a week before, joked with the nurses and the patients in the adjoining beds, and ate eagerly. Here and there old patients, thin and defeated, grabbed the food handed to them and almost before the trays had reached their knees began gobbling up the meal. Their eyes glowed with the greed of hunger, for they had known hunger a long time, and the purposes of living had died out one by one until only the drive to still that hunger was left.

They exchanged good-natured banter—comparing food, appetites, belly-fullness. Sitting upright in his bed was Tom Brennan, his right hand swathed in white gauze and three fingers just peeping out. On his lap rested a large, grey-yellow plate with the remnants of a large turkey drumstick. The surface of the plate was bare save for staining streaks of cranberry red through the narrow ridges of stiffening yellow turnip and gravy-brown mashed potatoes. In his left hand Tom held a large slice of mince pie out of which he had bitten a huge mouthful. The prune-colored juice dripped comfortably over the stubbled chin.

"Merry Christmas, Brennan. How's everything?" asked Ford, laying a friendly hand on Tom's shoulder. A fleeting grin lightened Brennan's dull face.

"Gee, Doc, I certainly am glad dat opyration wasn't on my ol' breadbasket!"

Smitty stepped briskly into the ward, dressed in street clothing. His lithe, muscular body was apparent beneath his snug fitting dark suit. Ford left Brennan's side to meet him.

"News for you, Benny," greeted Smitty. "I'm leaving the hospital right away. You know I was going back to Cooperstown, up-State. Well, I received a telegram a little while ago, asking me to come at once. The chief surgeon at our little hospital up there has pneumonia and they want me to help out. I 'phoned Hartley and he said it would be all right—he'd fix it up with our Medical Board. Swell of him, wasn't it?"

"Yes—it's fine—but of course you know I—we all—hate to see you go."

"Oh, I'll be down here bothering you soon—and maybe now you'll be house-surgeon again for a few hours. So long, Benny," and he held out his hand. Then he walked to Tom's bed, automatically took up the bedside chart, noted that his temperature was normal and with deft fingers examined, almost caressed, the accurately applied gauze bandage which covered the site of the operation. He gave Tom one of his quick, reassuring, generous smiles and inquired: "Any pain?"

"Not much, thanks, Doc. Nope, and it didn't hoit much at de opyration neither. I heerd de big soigin when he said after you got through—'Not bad, Smitty! you done a good job'. Thanks a lot, Doc."

"Sorry I shan't be able to see you again. But you'll be all right and Dr. Ford, here, will dress the wound. Well, good luck, Tom! Now have another piece of pie and Merry Christmas!"

II

THE BOTTLE OF CHAMPAGNE

The *Pschorr-Bräu* Restaurant in Munich about the year
1909 served as unofficial headquarters for the little group
of American doctors studying at the various clinics of the
University. To be sure the group was not dignified with
a *"Stammtisch"*—a special table such as was regularly reserved for two or three of the German Student Corps with
a banner of its own insignia and colors held aloft by a
bronze figure in the center of the table. However, if a
newcomer looking for Americans inquired of any of the
brisk waitresses bustling through the hall she would smilingly point to an undistinguished table near the window.

For years this table had been theirs because it was still
considered good form to complete the American training
in medicine with study at the famous clinics abroad—that
is, if the young medico's father happened to have the where-
withal and was indulgently disposed. The informal bunch
at the *Pschorr-Bräu* was forever changing. Transients were
always drifting in—usually older doctors from small towns
in the States taking post-graduate courses for a few months
in Vienna or Berlin after which they would return home
to label themselves specialists. But the nucleus of the group
consisted of men recently graduated from the better hospitals in America who had attached themselves to an interna-
tionally known physician to learn thoroughly the methods
of a single man. Because of the awakening interest in psychiatry some one was usually studying at the modern psychiatric clinic, now important because of the famed Pro-

fessor Emil Kraepelin who had come there recently from Heidelberg.

Around the convivial table the men aired their varied interests, goals and opinions in medicine, morals and politics. Of course, there was always sure to be disagreement on one subject or another but on one thing there was unanimity—that the beer in the *Pschorr-Bräu* was the best in all Bavaria, better even than the sweetish, thick, brown Würzburger whose praises at that time were being sung in the rollicking song "Down where the Würzburger flows".

One sunny spring day Ford was sitting at the American table where at the moment Kathy, a buxom, rosy-cheeked waitress in a simple black dress, was clearing away the dishes left by the students who had just departed. Ford lingered on, smoking a cheap Hamburg cigar, content to relax after a sumptuous meal of roast pork, sauerkraut, heavy brown bread and light brown beer. The one other occupant of the table was Harris, an unpretentious little man with large gold-rimmed glasses and a recently acquired scant black Vandyke beard which he had the habit of fingering incessantly.

The restaurant, with its dark paneling and low ceiling, was hazy with smoke and redolent with spicy fried food and beer. Ford was feeling expansive but Harris, with his penchant for long-winded accounts of cases he had seen and quoting authorities, was discouraging company. Ford stifled a yawn and had just about made up his mind to leave when the heavy oak doors were pushed open and in sauntered Chris Moore, a casual, irresponsible youngster from Ohio who was sampling his medical way through the clinics, cafes and cuisines of Europe. Behind him appeared—of all people!—Nasmyth.

Ford sprang to his feet, a delighted smile on his face. "Smitty, you old son-of-a-gun," he cried, gripping his friend's hand. "What on earth are you doing here?"

"So far just drinking beer but Moore tells me I can have no basis to qualify as an expert until I have had a few litres of this saloon's special brand."

"That's about the only thing on which you can take Moore's judgment," winked Benny, and turning to the buxom Kathy said, *"Ein Dunkles for der Herr Doktor."* "And now what are you, of all people, doing over here, Smitty? The last man I ever expected to see."

"To tell you the truth, it's the last place I ever expected to find myself two months ago. I went back to Cooperstown the day after that last operation at Bellevue—the amputation you steered my way the day before Christmas. Remember it, Benny?"

"Never will I forget that bleary-eyed old fellow gulping his third piece of pie."

"Well, I thought I was settled up there for life. I was doing all right, too. I had an appointment as adjunct surgeon to our hospital—a well equipped place with plenty of opportunity. Then I got a letter from Hartley asking me to see him in New York. Of course, I suspected that something was brewing. Well, the old boy ended by asking me to become his assistant in private and said he had a place for me on the visiting staff at St. James. You know he runs St. James."

"That's great, Smitty. I knew something like that was just bound to turn up for you sooner or later. The drinks are on me."

"You're on. Now let me tell you how it all happened. Lately Hartley has been particularly interested in lung surgery—thinks the field offers enormous possibilities. And he believes the clinic here is one of the best along those lines today. So he sent me over—I'll say this is beer. How do you say it when you want another—'*Dunkel*'—and am I content that the clinic is in this cozy nest of Munich and not in some Godforsaken, frozen place up in Prussia where you have to goose-step right up to the operating table. But you haven't told me about yourself, Benny," Nasmyth said, letting the lid of his stein clank shut. "What brings you to Munich outside of these foaming mugs?"

"Psychiatry. And now I guess you'll think I'm completely off my trolley."

Chris Moore wiped his mouth with the back of his hand and tilted his chair back. "Imagine a guy wanting to run a boarding house for a lot of loonies. Or is it to be a country club for drunks? Say, I've got an idea for this sanitarium of yours, Benny. Why not call it Idlewild for wild idlers. Maybe you'll get me some time."

"Hell," Ford retorted, "you don't know what you're talking about." Turning to his friend Nasmyth he addressed himself earnestly. "Mental crackups are avoidable if only they can be treated in time. What we need is free clinics so that we can diagnose the cases and treat the patients before they go too far."

"You talk as if lunatics had a disease like pneumonia or t.b.," Chris scoffed.

"That's exactly what I do mean, but don't call them lunatics," Ford said sharply.

"I knew a man once . . ." Harris began timidly.

But Nasmyth was speaking. "Sounds just like you, Benny. There never was a man who could break more needles and get a rougher edge on a scalp wound—or who took more interest in his fellow men, not to mention the women. Benny had that sympathetic approach. If he had only been half as good a technician in the operating room as he was on midnight rounds. . . . He had a notion of thinking as much about the man who had broken his leg as about the leg that the man had broken. Now I'll admit that such stuff isn't important in fractures, but with those fliver appendectomies and some of those funny bellyaches, it's sometimes hard to say whether the bellyache has got the patient or the patient is just bellyaching. That's where Benny came in."

"Ever heard this one, Smitty? Here's where you come in.

'In heaven his delight is
For he is with the blest
For he had appendicitis
And the surgeons did the rest'."

"Yeh, I've heard that one before. You know, fellows, Benny used to take a two page history on a clear case of fractured skull. Sometimes I think he should have been a reporter."

"Well, I suppose we fellows in psychiatry should have the reporter's contact with life, his nose for news and some of his human sympathy which he usually conceals so well under his bluntness and damned persistence. Just now I am working on a case at the clinic which had quite a little newspaper notice. A mild-mannered young woman was arrested for making a terrible fracas out at the cemetery the other day. She started to shout and dance on a new grave."

"*Dunkel!*" Chris Moore called to Kathy, holding up four fingers. "Was it a seven veil Salome or hootchy-kootchy? Let's have the bare facts." Moore was all attention.

Ford sipped his beer. "No, nothing like that. She came from a good family and was extraordinary shy and retiring."

"Drunk, I suppose," Chris conjectured.

Ford smiled at the way Chris revealed his own preoccupations. "No, she was cold sober as well as completely dressed."

"Then what was the crime?" Moore demanded. "Did she attack someone?"

"No, she was just dancing," said Ford, enjoying a slight retaliation for Moore's scoffing.

The latter was at the end of his patience. "Is there any law out here against dancing?"

"I guess that depends on the time and the place. This girl was doing her dancing in a cemetery while a funeral service was being held not twenty feet away. She was throwing herself about and shrieking at the top of her lungs. All at once she took a champagne bottle and smashed it over a gravestone."

"What'd she want to do that for?" Moore inquired.

"I don't think she wanted to, not, that is, the way you and I choose to do a thing. I'd say it was a matter of compulsion. That apparently was the judge's conclusion because she was sent to a psychiatric clinic before he would decide her sentence. The courts out here have been doing that sort of thing quite often lately."

"What happened to the young lady?" Harris asked as if thereby to move from the periphery into contact with the others.

"Do you mean before or after her arrest?" Ford asked.

Harris looked nonplussed but he rallied quickly. "Did something happen before?"

"Tell us about it," Nasmyth invited, leaning back and folding his arms comfortably.

"Do you fellows really want to hear about her?"

"Nothing better to do until three o'clock," said Moore looking leisurely at his watch and taking another cigarette from his shiny cherry-wood case.

Ford lit a new cigar which burned briskly and unevenly. "Well, there's a long story behind that kid's wild explosion. They gave me the case to work up because there's an American twist to the tale—at least it began in America and the girl speaks English as well as German. During her excitement after she was admitted, she mixed up the two like a lettuce and tomato salad."

"Was she pretty?" asked Moore, always interested in the female.

"Oh, you wouldn't take a second look at this one—she's odd looking and odd—utterly confused. Her name is Gisella Schultz and she's about twenty-five years old and is still half a child. She belongs to that group of eccentrics who gather out there in Schwabing on the other side of the Ludwig-strasse Arch. The same gang who drift to Greenwich Village. Only this crowd is more cosmopolitan, people from all over the world, who could not get along in Rio or Stockholm, or God knows where. They have talents of a minor sort in sculpture, writing or painting, and this one does water-colors—she isn't really bright at all—just what the French call disequilibrated."

"What's she doing out here, then," asked Smitty as he clapped down the metal top of his beer stein.

"She's been living here for seven years with a Dutch girl, also an ex-patriate, who's a bit older but every bit as queer. Each of them is living on a small monthly remittance from home. I guess their families were glad to be freed of the responsibility for them."

"Whose grave was she dancing on?" asked Harris in his solemn, pedantic voice.

"That's just the point," answered Ford. "It was her step-mother's freshly dug grave and the whole performance turned out to be a wild if solitary celebration of the death of the old woman—right in broad daylight. It all happened a little while after she had read the death notice in a three day old Munich paper. The lady's name was Emma Schultz. The story opens in Milwaukee, Wisconsin, in the early 1890's. Now remember that the deceased was the second Mrs. Schultz, the kid's step-mother. Gisella is the only child of the first marriage of her father, Waldemar, that's German enough, isn't it? He was a prosperous buggy- and carriage-maker over in Wisconsin. The first Mrs. Schultz was a frail little woman whom the girl always called Mutti and who became a chronic invalid at the time of Gisella's birth—it appears to have been due to a long drawn-out septic heart condition."

"There are such cases reported in the literature," ventured Harris irrelevantly, stroking his beard and looking self-conscious.

"Yes, I suppose so," continued Benny. "At all events, the marriage soon became one in name only. As for Gisella, she had inherited her mother's feeble constitution and slight build. To make matters worse, the care, indulgence, and overprotection which the mother, living in the shadow of her own death and with no other interest in life, gave her only child almost killed Gisella. Her stomach became too sensitive through mushy and improper food, her bowels sluggish and her puny body remained weak and underdeveloped because of lack of exercise and outdoor air during her early years."

"You'll have us crying in our beer, Benny. What has that to do with champagne, excepting that it's dry," flipped Moore stretching himself, with an extra long yawn.

"Maybe it will bubble up a bit after a while. But I'll try to spill it quickly for your benefit. So, let's get on. Between her mother's caution and the prohibitions of various doctors which her mother followed religiously, the poor kid grew up apart from other children—too delicate for their games, too shy to associate with them. The attention and devotion of her mother, an ardent and sacrificing love, gradually created and nurtured the only responses akin to love which the pampered but unfortunate child ever felt."

"Looks to me just like a spoiled kid. Seen plenty of them. Why all the tears and fuss," droned Moore.

"Pipe down," exclaimed Smitty. "Let's hear it through."

"Well, we'll continue with the consent of the gentleman from Ohio," said Ford. "As the years passed the mother continued to waste away, and finally was barely able to stand the exertion of moving from her chair. Then this woman, Emma, the widow of Heinrich, the child's mother's brother, began to show great solicitude for the invalid—visited her ever so often and when she became bedridden sometimes stayed overnight to nurse her."

"Great sacrifice but no action yet," interjected Chris Moore, "just a darn dull story. Where are those bubbles you promised?"

"Cheer up, the worst is yet to come. But I notice you listening just the same—I am not wearying you," retorted Benny. "True, there's not much fun in most psychiatric tales. You'd surely know that if you had talked with this distraught twenty-five year old kid when they brought her into the clinic and I saw her there. She kept on sobbing piteously looking at me through her thick spectacles, and imploring over and over again, 'Help me, *Herr Doktor*, help me. Don't let them send me away. I'm not crazy'.

"Most of what I've been telling you came out piecemeal in German. It had been her mother language in thought and word, for although she had been born and grew up in Milwaukee, she spoke English with a German accent, structure and idiom. After a while, she learned that I was an American, she clung to me tenaciously as though the sound of English words awoke all the latent thoughts of protection associated with her native land.

" 'Why did you do it?' I asked her after I had gained her confidence.

" 'I couldn't help it, Herr Doktor. I knew it was wrong but I could do nothing else, I had to do it. For years I thought of it, nothing else was on my mind—now my vow came true'.

" 'Which vow, Gisella?' I asked her.

" 'My revenge. Nobody knows it but now I will tell only you about it. You shall be the first one to know!'

"I'll try not to bother you fellows with too many details

or reproductions of Gisella's broken English. Her story, as she
told it, goes something like this:

" 'I was fifteen years old when Mutti got real sick and
Tante Emma came to the house all the time. Mutti's brother
used to be her husband, he was dead. Before, Papa always
used to leave Mutti and me alone during the day but now he
began to come home for lunch sometimes and sometimes
not to go down town to the *Turnverein* at nights any more
to play pinochle with his friends. He seemed to be getting
old and Tante Emma began to look after him a lot—made
coffee for him at nights with coffee cake. Mutti would be
choking and coughing in bed in the next room but Tante
Emma looked out more for Papa. I began to think she
wanted Mutti to die.'

" 'How did you ever come on such an idea?' I asked her.

" 'One day I heard her say to Mutti that she would soon
die. Why should she say that to her? Then one night through
a crack in the door I saw Tante Emma bend over Papa as
he drank his coffee and kiss him on his bald spot. Now I
knew why Emma wanted to seem to love Mutti. I hated her
with all my might'.

" 'I can understand that', I said to Gisella.

" 'That is not all, Herr Doktor. In the waste basket one day
I saw a letter torn up. It was written on Mutti's best blue
writing paper—I had given it to her for Christmas. That
night I pasted all the pieces together. It took me a long, long
time. The letter ended, you are my *lieber Schatz, Waldy—ich
liebe dich*—Emma. More and more my hatred grew. More it
grew as Mutti sat propped up high on pillows in the bed,
breathing harder every day, never sleeping at night.

" 'A curious, inquisitive child I was ever. Maybe Mutti
made me so and I now spent more and more time watching
Papa and Tante even when they thought me in bed. One
night I was watching through the door again. Tante held a

big green bottle with silver around the top. I heard a sound—
a loud pop—and I heard Emma laughing as she raised her
glass to Papa: "*Champagner*, Waldemar".'

" 'Is there nothing else?' I asked gently, though by this
time Gisella needed no encouragement to talk.

" 'Ja, Mutti was nearly dead. I was always looking and
sneaking about, and one day in the closet I found two new,
long paper boxes on the shelf—one with big square envelopes,
the other with printed cards. On them it read, "Mr. Waldemar Schultz and family wish to thank you for your very kind
expression of sympathy in their late bereavement".'

" 'Shocking,' I found myself murmuring under my breath",
said Ford. Then he continued: "Gisella did not appear to
notice my exclamation of repugnance. She had by now become so thoroughly engrossed in her own story.

" 'One night Mutti died. Then Tante Emma stayed on to
keep house for Papa. I always hated her—the more she pre-
tended to love me the more I hated her.'

" 'Did you grieve when your mother died?' I asked her.

" 'No, not grief—not for long. Maybe I did not love her as
much as I should. But Emma I hated. Then I hated her
brother, Freddy Heinz, who used to come up to the house
after a while from his business and eat lunch, and I hated her
nieces and everything about the Heinz family.'

" 'Did you ever mention any of this to anybody?' I asked.

" '*Nein*, never a word, Herr Doktor. I was a sly one, ever
trying to find out what the old folks were doing—"sly Gisella"
they used to call me. I am that way. When I saw what Emma
had in her mind I spent all the time snooping and spying.
It did no good for a long time. But I kept on watching from
closets, from the yard, through the windows of Emma's room,
through the keyholes. Then one night, about six months after
Mutti died, what did I see—Emma in her room with another
green bottle and from it she poured some of the bubbling
champagne into a glass. She held it before her, smiling, drank

it all alone, and this time, she laughed all to herself. What do you think I found then, Herr Doktor?'

" 'I can't guess'.

" 'In the same old closet I found new boxes with cards. It said on them, "Mr. Fred Heinz announces the marriage of his sister, Emma, to Mr. Waldemar Schultz, Milwaukee, October 20, 1901." Sure enough, about two months after I first saw the cards, Tante Emma and Papa got married. I knew nothing about it, except the announcements, until it was all over. Then Papa said to me one day, "You have a new Mutti, Gisi". He looked awful old and not so happy. You see, Herr Doktor, how it was.'

" 'Yes, you certainly had a very difficult time, didn't you, Gisella?'

" 'Nothing would come through my thoughts but hate. Then I soon heard that Tante Emma was not well. She kept mum about her illness until I found it out all by myself. It was high blood pressure she had. I asked the doctor what was good for her. She must rest, he said, and above all no excitement.'

" 'And what did you do then?' I asked the girl who, however, needed no prodding.

" 'Oh, I spent a whole lot of time reading in some old medical books Papa had in the library. I found out what to do to cure high blood pressure and then I did the opposite to Papa's wife. I'd get our cook, Lena, to spoil the dinner so that Emma would get raving mad. Emma would always be forgetting where she had left her handbag. I would steal it and hide it in a room where she had been so that she might think that she had left it there. It made great excitement for her when she could not find it. She would run around like mad and get red and purple in the face.'

" 'Didn't you feel a little ashamed of yourself, even a wee little bit, acting so mean to the sick old woman and making her blood pressure go up', I asked.

" 'It wasn't my fault. I was glad. I hated her. She was a wicked old thing. I hated Emma Heinz that bad—but also the Heinzes hated me.'

" 'Didn't you feel a teeny, weeny bit sorry for your Aunt Emma', I coaxed.

"The girl hung her head and began to whimper. 'Sometimes at night when everybody was asleep I'd be awake in my bed and cry a long time all by myself because I knew I was bad too.'

"I waited for a time and then asked, 'What did your father do about all your mischief?'

" 'Papa was dull and sleepy nearly all the time—he had a bad heart, too, the doctor said. One day he got a stroke in his arm and leg and could not talk either—in four days he died.'

" 'How old did you say you were then?'

" 'I was just seventeen.'

"I am sure any of you fellows would say that the twenty-five year old girl hardly looks more than fifteen now," said Benny turning to the attentive little group at the table.

"Would you call it a case of arrested development?" asked Smitty.

"Well, yes and no—she certainly looks like an undergrown woman and mentally she is very immature," replied Benny. "I think that you'll agree with me about this from what follows.

" 'You see, Herr Doktor,' Gisella told me, 'Papa left nearly all his money to Emma. To me he left what they call a trust fund, only twenty-five thousand dollars. Freddy Heinz saw to it that it should be that way. The money from it is not much for a girl like me who never learned to work and knew nothing. Then something happened. Freddy Heinz, I cannot call him an uncle, he started to hate me. He wanted to take from me the money which Papa left me—he wanted to kill me.'

" 'Are you quite sure that your aunt's brother really want-

ed to kill you? Maybe you only thought this was so', I finally
said to her in order to find out how much of this story she
might admit to be her imagination.

" 'No', she replied with great heat, 'he hated me. All the
Heinzes, they hate me. They wanted I should die.' "

"Isn't that an unusual turn, Benny?" asked Smitty thought-
fully. "This idea that the people whom the girl hated should
want to do her harm."

"Not as uncommon as you might think", replied Benny.
"A case of the pot calling the kettle black—you know how it
is. For example, just today on rounds the Geheimrat called
down an old soak. The beer-guzzler accused his wife of being
unfaithful and Kraepelin said, 'You get drunk, come home
and can't do anything with her, then think that she runs
around with other men instead of blaming yourself'."

"Takes a thief to catch a thief. I should know", chirped
Moore.

"Something like that", said Ford, "and sometimes a fellow
who cheats another would rather think that the other fellow
is out to do him. It kinda justifies his own attitude.—Now, to
come back to Gisella, I tried to pin the kid down. Asked her
how she could be so certain of all the enmity and animosity
against her. Then she told me this incident which shows
how far her morbid idea had gone.

" 'Herr Doktor', she said earnestly, 'listen to me. Freddy
Heinz had a boy, Walter, was his name. He was just as old
as me. One day there was a high school dance. I did not
want to go but I had a teacher, Miss Wagram. She taught
art. I was good at drawing and I liked Miss Wagram. When
Mutti died and Emma married Papa she seemed to know I
was feeling sad. Miss Wagram made me go to the dance. I
knew hardly anybody there and so most of the time I just
sat at the side of the wall. By and by my cousin, Walter Heinz,
passed by me dancing with a girl. She looked at me. Then I
heard Walter say something—hang it—or something. Then I

knew. Uncle Freddy wanted that Walter should hang me.'

" 'Did you really believe that?' I asked her.

" 'Yes, maybe just only perhaps, but you will see I was right. Miss Wagram went to France every three years to talk French conversation and go to art school. She asked me if I would come over with her. It made me very happy to go with her. But Tante Emma wanted that I should go, too. She wanted to get rid of me.'

" 'But why should your Aunt Emma wish to send you away if she and her brother and Walter were so anxious to kill you? Doesn't that seem a little inconsistent,' I asked.

" 'I don't know—but they did. Now listen, Herr Doktor. Once in Paris in a little street near the Rue du Cherche Midi I saw a young man who looked like Walter. He followed me.' She hesitated a moment. 'Yes, it was Walter.'

" 'How could you be sure of your suspicion? Did you talk with him?' I asked.

" 'No, I did not even look. I was afraid. But who else could it be—nobody else would follow me', she insisted irrelevantly.

" 'I think you imagined it,' I told her. What I said made no impression on her. I doubt if it registered at all. After a minute or so I took up the question differently.

" 'Are you given much to fancying things, Gisella?'

"She looked at me and stared blankly and absent-mindedly. Finally she said, 'All the time ever since I was a little girl I would fancy. And then I had one fancy every night and in the day time, too, when any one about me scolded.'

" 'Will you tell it to me,' I suggested.

" 'Well,' then she said hesitatingly, 'I used to fancy that I was all alone in a big, big house up on a hill with a big wall around it—and everything was there and I didn't need to ask anything from anybody. But I didn't have to do anything to get everything and I didn't have to worry about anybody outside.'

" 'Quite self-sufficient, weren't you, Gisella,' I said gently. She seemed as self-absorbed as if she were repeating that very fantasy or something like it at the moment.

"Does the literature have names for ideas like that?" inquired Harris meekly, again attempting to leave the periphery by a show of interest.

"Sure", replied Benny. "Most likely it would be something like a visual illusion or an hallucination.

" 'Any more fancies except the one about the house,' I asked her but she did not reply. When I pointed out that she had no reason or evidence that the man she thought had followed her wished in anyway to harm her, she came out of her abstraction and became greatly aroused.

" '*Ja, ja,* that's what Miss Wagram said too,' she screamed. 'But why did all my terrible fear of the Heinzes come back to me again if it wasn't Walter. They must have hated me or why did they send him to follow me. After that I could not sleep. At nights I would dream of Mutti and Emma and big green bottles of champagne, sometimes as big as the Eiffel Tower. Miss Wagram got all frightened about my brooding and worrying and nervousness. I did not want to go home with her because Tante Emma and the Heinzes were after me there, too. She sent a cable to Freddy Heinz who said that it was all right if I stayed over here, but I was too afraid to stay in Paris where I saw Walter. He might get me there. So, all alone, I came to München and here I found my Dutch friend. She hates her step-father like I hate Papa's wife. We paint trees and houses and beautiful things. America, I have almost forgotten, Herr Doktor.'

" 'How do you live?'

" 'Every month Papa's money comes from Freddy Heinz, but he hates me just because I hate Emma—just as I always have from that time of the bottle of champagne—never has it not been there—always I wanted to see her dead. At nights

out here in München I would lie in my bed and think of
all sorts of nasty things to say to her to make her mad so
she would die quick of blood pressure. I said them to myself
and I would get excited fine and dandy.'

" 'Didn't you ever try to check all these bitter feelings? Did
it ever occur to you that it might not be good for you, yourself, to keep thinking all those mean things?'

" 'Never, never', she cried with mounting excitement. Her
pale, childlike, peaked face flushed, her eyes blazed through
the thick lenses. Suddenly she jumped from her chair and
shrieked: 'I read in the paper that Papa's wife had died in
Bad Nauheim and they had buried her in the graveyard
right here in München—in München because her sister lives
here. I got all wild and happy.'

" 'What were you so glad about, Gisella', I asked, for I was
puzzled about the connection between her delusions and
the scene at the cemetery.

" 'Look, Herr Doktor,' she screamed, 'in the bottom of my
trunk for seven years I carried a green bottle with silver about
the cork in a little straw basket. The very first day in Paris
with Miss Wagram I bought it for eight francs and hid it in
my trunk. Now the day had come. *Gott helfe mir*. I took
the bottle and went to the graveyard in a street car, I think.
I do not remember anything but something told me soon I
would find Emma's grave.'

"Her words now came so fast that they tumbled over one
another and at times were hard to understand.

" 'How did your mind seem,' I asked the question at the
time mainly to interrupt the rapid flow of words. She did
not heed me but rushed on.

" 'My mind went like lightning. I was all mixed up in my
mind but I think a new funeral was close by and a priest
saying prayers. It did not matter. I danced. I think I yelled
verdammt, verdammt, and I smashed the bottle on the
stones in the earth over her grave. Please, oh please, Herr

Doktor', she sobbed frantically throwing herself to the floor and clutching my knees, 'please, do not let them send me away'."

Benny relit the short, charred stump of his cigar and blew circles of smoke into the still air of the nearly deserted cafe. The little group at the table remained still and thoughtful. Chris Moore broke the silence:

"Well, I'd say it is a swell story—a scoop for Benny they'd call it on the *Akron News Dispatch*. I guess you're just a reporter after all, Benny. The only difference is that instead of having to chase all around town to gather up the dirt, you have it brought right to your own door and I suppose that some day you'll get paid for listening to it. That's just what I'd expect of a lazy bum like you."

Chris looked at his watch. He picked up a green Tyrolean peasant's hat which he had bought the first day in Munich, and drawing from his pocket a pair of cream colored pigskin gloves ornamented with heavy black stitching, fashionable just then in Paris, said, "So long, you fellows, I am off to the *Café Luitpold*. I am late all right but she'll be sitting and waiting at a marble topped table. That's one thing about these chickens over here; they always wait for you if they know you'll feed them," and he strolled leisurely out of the door whistling the waltz from the Merry Widow.

"How would you account for that graveyard act?" asked Smitty with more than a complimentary show of interest. "Sounds to me like she might have been drunk."

"Something like it, I guess, but not on beer or wine," replied Benny. "Intoxicated by her own wild joy of triumph and revenge. She was about as incoherent and irresponsible as if she had drained every drop from that big green bottle instead of spattering its foam over the dead woman's grave. One grand dry-jag."

"But what would the diagnosis be," asked Harris, again

like an ambitious schoolboy seeking to ingratiate himself
with a teacher whom he feared and envied.

"Oh, probably a mild paranoia—ideas of persecution."

"Thanks," he said diffidently. "I guess I better be going
back to the library and look up the literature on the subject," and the insecure little man slid away from the table
nervously passing his fingers through the scraggly beard as
he drew away.

After he left both men sat quietly for a time, each lost in
his own thoughts. Smitty spoke first, admiration in his voice.
"Yes, I can see the whole thing as distinctly as I might see an
abscess which I suspected was in a liver and which I had
finally exposed after a long and tedious dissection. I understand the girl's plight now. What are they going to do with
that kid, Benny?" he asked with a genuine interest. And to
indicate how completely absorbed he had been in the story,
he smilingly pointed to the glass mugs standing on the table
before them, dry and empty, except for a thin layer of the
dark beer covering the bottoms.

"Well, Professor Kraepelin, the *Geheimrat* at the *Klinik,*
is a 'capacity', as they call them out here. He's a gruff old
customer, but human and canny. Right now he is taking
care of the King of this Bavarian state who has been hopelessly insane for ever so many years—spends most of his time
peeling potatoes, they say. So Kraepelin's word counts for
something with the authorities here. He will write a long
protocol to some high judge which, in the end, will only say
that he regards this pale, furtive young woman as a child
mentally under sixteen years, her act as the violence of immaturity, and that as an irresponsible kid she should not be
punished or sent to prison. His opinion goes a long way."

"Can't you do anything for her?" asked Smitty.

"Of course," answered Benny. "We will try to straighten
out her confused thinking at the hospital, but I doubt if
we can change her too much in a short time. Eventually we

will send her back to the 'artistic set', as they call themselves, but who are mostly misfits on the fringe of lunacy. They are accustomed to indulging one another's indolence, peculiarities and vanities, and expecting to be forgiven by the rest of the world because they think they are artists."

"Guess it's an interesting specialty, but there's nothing hilarious about it. Not for me. How did you ever think of taking it up?" This time Smitty held up his stein to Kathy as she passed. "Another *Dunkel,* Benny?" he asked. "Why do you want to go into psychiatry?"

"I guess, since you ordered two steins, you really want to hear. It was like this—Rankin picked me out while I was on his service at Bellevue. Said I had talent for the work and his remark struck a response way down in me—made me realize my interest in people. Did I ever tell you that it was Balzac's *Country Doctor* which made me want to study medicine? Or, maybe it was my mother's headaches which I remember as a little boy that are back of my interest in neurotics. Anyway I think it's the coming specialty."

"So is surgery of the chest. I'll stick to that," responded Smitty.

"And we won't be rivals and now on the basis of that let me introduce you to some white radishes, black bread and sweet butter. It's a great combination which I first tasted in Munich and my days here are numbered. Funds are running low and no discerning, philanthropically-minded Hartley wishes to endow my latent talents."

"I suppose you are going on with this sort of thing when you get back home?"

"Surely, and it seems that something new and big is stirring in this field in Vienna. Perhaps you recall 'Maggie' Magoffin from New York. He's gone into neuropathology. 'Maggie' stopped over for a few days on his way home. He told me that a fellow in Vienna named Freud has the goods about hysteria. This Freud doesn't rate very high in his home town because he is not a regular university professor and besides his ideas don't sit too well—far too much about dreams and sex. But I'll lay my money on 'Maggie's' say-so. Maybe I'll buy one of Freud's books before I leave this burg."

"Will I be seeing you again, Benny?"

"Sure. How would you like to come with me next weekend to Tegernsee—it's a wonderful lake up in the Bavarian Alps not too far from here. I can get hold of a couple of bicycles and we will pedal down leisurely to a plain but comfortable inn which I know—climb a baby mountain, do a lot of loafing and some dancing—gossip on the terrace by the lake—and forget about the clinics."

III

THE BOARDERS

The railway station for the Eastern State Hospital was a weather-beaten, bilious-colored little house located some thirty miles from New York City on a spur which branched off from the main-line. When young Dr. Ford stepped off the two-car train one sunny June morning, he learned from the driver of a shabby surrey waiting at the broken wooden platform that the main buildings of the institution were a mile distant and that the charge would be fifty cents. The way followed a dirt road briefly and then turned off on the asphalt highway which curved gently among low hills until it reached a stretch with a stone wall at the left. "That's her", said the driver as buildings of many sizes and shapes and here and there a spire came to view through the green of bushes and trees. Indeed very few of the people passing along the highway on holidays in their popular new Model T touring cars were aware that in these buildings behind the wall and its verdant fringe the State of New York was caring for many thousands of its mentally ill patients.

During the first decade of this century, when physicians after finishing their internships in general hospitals began to prepare themselves for the specialty of mental disease, a number of young men chose the Eastern State Hospital as the most desirable place for training and experience. Dr. Ford was one of these. "Maggie" Magoffin, the neuropathologist, had praised it at great length to Ford when they had met in Munich and had been enthusiastic about its modern spirit and gifted leaders. He claimed that its standards and

63

ideals equalled the best that he had seen in the famed psychiatric hospitals of Europe.

When the surrey turned off the main road, past two high stone pillars which marked the entrance to the grounds of the hospital, the bright green lawns, the carefully trimmed privet hedges, the bushy beds of cannas bordered with gay petunias gave no hint to the visitor of the disappointments and frustrations, of the agony and human suffering which the red brick walls of the old buildings confined and concealed. The horse slowed to walk when he struck an upgrade leading to the Administration Building and as Ford looked out upon the clean gravel paths bounded by low hedges, he sensed a resemblance of the grounds to the carefully kept parks of European spas. He carried a letter of recommendation from Dr. Rankin, one of his former professors, to Dr. Forrest, the Director of the medical work in the enormous institution. Forrest turned out to be a formally pleasant man of forty-five, tall, stout, pink cheeked and baldish with a fringe of closely cropped greying red hair. He was evidently satisfied with Ford's introduction and qualifications, for after a brief interview he sent him with a note to Dr. Ralph Perkins, the physician in charge of the Admission Ward.

Perkins, known to everyone at old Eastern as "Pop" Perkins, received Ford neutrally. Indeed, Ford was soon to learn that neutrality was the key-note of Perkins' approach to life and his work. He had already spent twenty-five years at that very hospital in the daily routine of his profession, developing a safe philosophy of always choosing the middle course. It mattered not to his middle course mind that he never arrived anywhere. What was most important to him was that it avoided landing him at any point where he might encounter too much trouble or responsibility. His voice had acquired a bland, almost weary, tone; his words were slow and measured.

"Glad to meet you, Dr. Ford," he said without a trace of enthusiasm. "I heard about you; heard you've been to Europe and are coming to work in the Admission Ward. One of the new kind of men we're now getting here at Eastern who want experience and don't expect to stay here long—all heading for private practice."

"That's right", answered Ford.

"Well, we don't mind. Plenty of new cases are sent out here to the Admission Ward from Bellevue every other week —too many of them—some odd customers that would interest you scientifically. I'm going there now—want to come along?"

As they walked down on the path they passed an elderly, spare, bald-headed man industriously trimming the high hedges with a pair of large shears. His work was nearly perfect. He stopped clipping for a moment to mop his tanned face with a large, coarse handkerchief, and stared blankly at the physicians. Perkins allowed his measured gait to slow down to a stop.

"Still at it, Denny," Perkins said to the dull man who appeared fatigued by his labor and stood looking at him with the sharp shears dangling from his hand.

No sign of recognition or response showed on the face of the hedge-trimmer.

"I'm rooting for you," drawled Perkins whose whining monotone came so spontaneously and naturally that it freed his frank praise of any vestige of patronage or condescension.

A fleeting grin of appreciation now appeared on the industrious man's face as he turned back to his task but without saying a word.

"Not so deteriorated as some folks think," said Perkins in his noncommittal, unvarying voice.

"Is he a patient?" asked Ford, astonished that an insane person should be allowed at large with so dangerous a weapon as the shears.

"Yeah," replied Perkins. "That's one, too," pointing to a

man who was standing on a steep roof assisting in repairing it.

"What's wrong with him?" asked Ford, nodding in the direction of the man who had returned to clipping the hedge borders.

"An old dementia praecox, I suspect. He's been here God knows how long—longer than I have—and works like that all the time. I once tried to find out what was wrong with him but nobody seemed to know exactly. Lots of chronic patients here sometimes get lost in the shuffle. All I can say is he must be crazy—nobody but a crazy man would work as hard as he does and stay about this place. It's his boarding house, I guess, and he's been in it so long he's afraid to get out—a border for a boarder." There was no change in Perkins' listless voice to indicate that he had intentionally made a pun. He drawled on. "There are a lot of them around here like that—not all of them patients either."

Then as he lapsed into a silence which discouraged interruption, Ford's thoughts reverted to Chris Moore's jibe some three months previously in Munich, when he mentioned to him his own hope of owning a sanitarium some day—about "running a boarding house for a lot of loonies". The idea seemed, from that moment, to lose all its allure for him.

Without a word Perkins suddenly turned around and walked back a hundred yards or more to take a narrow cinder path to the right. "There's an old Irish woman, a patient, who has diagnosed the situation here pretty well. I'll take you past her ward—if she's there we'll surely get her opinion —she's been announcing it to every doctor who passes her window for the past six months."

They proceeded along the path for a short distance to where it passed a weather-stained, low, brick building. At an open corner-window, peering through the perpendicular iron bars which guarded it, stood the old woman—her white hair dishevelled, her old eyes bright with excitement. When she spied the physicians approaching, she began shouting: "Arrh, and it's all very well for you byes to be comin' along here a-laughin' and a-smilin' and if it wasn't for us ye'd all lose yer jobs, ye'd all lose yer jobs, ye'd all lose yer jobs."

She repeated this over and over again, shouting it after the doctors when they had passed until her voice could no longer be heard in the distance.

"Not so crazy," drawled Perkins as he turned to take a diagonal shortcut over a field to the Admission Ward. "Maybe some day there won't be jobs for us," he resumed gravely after several minutes. "I suppose you heard a lot about the new blood test for syphilis and the arsenic cure—606—over in Europe. It sounds like the real thing," he whined.

"It certainly does," agreed Ford as he adjusted himself to Perkins' slow pace. The latter muttered a little to himself as he walked toward his long accustomed place of work—his unpretentious niche in the scheme of things.

They reached the door of another single-storied, long, narrow building—the male Admission Ward. Perkins, with slow deliberation, drew from his pocket a keyring from which dangled six or eight large keys—mostly brass. With one of these he unlocked the door and entered the hall of the building leaving Ford to follow. The air was heavy with the penetrating, acrid, stale smell of the human animal. It is an odor which clings to the walls of rooms continuously occupied by many people—jails, almshouses and mental hospitals.

On each side of the hall near the entrance were two small, meagerly furnished rooms which served as offices for the doctors. Perkins indicated that his own room was on the right nearest the ward. Through the partly open door of the room across the hall, Ford could hear a physician talking with a patient.

"That's Dr. Partridge's," said Perkins with a sour look.

"I'm going to give you the room next to his. We're short of men just now. We're always short. The people up at Albany won't pay enough to keep first-rate men here."

He turned without further comment to go through the plainly furnished sitting room which separated the doctors' offices from the ward. Ford followed. The ward, a room over one hundred feet long and perhaps thirty feet wide, contained rows of cast-iron beds on either side about six feet apart. Patients in rough hospital clothing were walking aimlessly about or sitting on chairs between the beds. As Perkins passed along, nodding to a trained nurse or an attendant, he stopped now and then, removed his glasses and chewed at the end of the steel shaft while he looked sharply at this or that patient. Many of them were bed-ridden, men who had had paralytic strokes; others had advanced paresis which the newly discovered arsenic drug, called 606, was perhaps destined to cure; others were very helpless old men with sadly vacant eyes; others, excited, talkative younger men, one of whom struggled and tossed in his irrational state under a canvas restraining sheet as he kept up a continuous stream of words.

Perkins paused before a young, dull looking individual with an oily complexion who lay motionless as if dead, then gently raised the youth's left arm and bent the forearm at the elbow to a right angle. It was allowed to stay in that position as though moulded of wax and the patient were not conscious of the doctor's move. "Catatonic praecox," remarked Perkins laconically to Ford.

One got the impression that the neutral doctor was as cautious and careful with his patients as he was with his words; that if he would take no new untried steps for their benefit, he would see to it that no harm or abuse came to them. The rosy-cheeked, kind-hearted, young Irish peasant girls and young men who served as attendants knew it, too.

Perkins returned leisurely and silently to the front of the

building, stepping noiselessly with his rubber-soled shoes, scrutinizing each patient carefully on the way out, adjusting the sideboards of a bed here and there; stopping for a minute or two to feel the pulse of a fast breathing, emaciated man; inspecting the dried lips and the parched mouth of a semi-delirious patient. To one such he offered a tin cup of water. His deliberation and imperturbability impressed the uneducated attendants without words from him that they were not to neglect any measures which he had prescribed for his deranged charges. As he passed out through the cheerless sitting room he again nodded and greeted neutrally each of the four or five patients who were idling there.

When Perkins and Ford reached Dr. Partridge's office they met him just coming out.

"Dr. Partridge," whined Perkins, "this is Dr. Ford who is going to work with us for a while." To the dreariness of his voice was now added sufficient coolness to reveal that Dr. Perkins had neither great love nor respect for his insignificant looking assistant.

Partridge, a thin man in the early thirties, wore his hair parted so that it separated his head longitudinally in the middle. He wore a fixed, mirthless grin which divided his face at right angles to the hair part. He had been christened Arthur Boyd Partridge, a name which lent itself to nicknames peculiarly appropriate to his character. From high-school days he had been dubbed "Party", or "Party-boy", or "Arty Party", and these names had stuck to him.

"Hello, Dr. Ford," he exclaimed with artificial cordiality. "Glad to welcome you. Hear you are just back from abroad with all the latest dope—hah, hah. I certainly am glad you came—we need a little life about this place. I'm progressive —hah, hah. By the way, did you bring your tennis shoes?"

"Not yet, why?"

"Well, you'll need them. If you want to stay on the Island these days you've got to wear them to sneak right up from

behind and catch those hidden complexes everybody is talking about—hah, hah. You've got to do it to keep up to date
—Jung's complexes, you know. By the way, did you see Jung
and Freud over there? Junk and Fraud I call them—hah,
hah."

"No, I barely heard of them in Munich—they weren't
geared to psychoanalysis at Kraepelin's place."

"I guess not—not progressive like us. Well, hidden complexes are all the rage now at Eastern. Did you hear that
Junk and Fraud are coming over soon—hah, hah. Going to
Worcester, Mass., where Adolf Meyer used to be before he
came here to New York State. Ad Meyer is what I call him
because I admire him so much. That is, sometimes you know,
when he's not too stiff on you—and then I don't Ad Meyer
him any more—hah, hah. Well, I'll see you at the staff house.
I quit working here early and take that time to keep up with
the literature. I'm reading Morton Prince right now. I'm
not staying at this shebang much longer—going into practice
soon."

At this point Perkins moved out of his office with a patient's history folder in his hand. "Doctor Partridge", he
drawled even more deliberately than usual, "I notice the
physical examination you made on that last patient is incom-
plete. Better finish it."

"Yes, sir", said Partridge obediently and he started off at
once toward the ward.

"He hasn't been staying here from the day he came five
years ago. Guess he'll be glad to stay on boarding here 'til
the day they transfer him and his blondined, rattle-brained
wife to some hospital upstate even deader than this," said
Perkins, giving Ford the merest indication of a smile. "You
know that Party-boy missed two broken ribs in the patient
he just examined. There was a special notation on the commitment blank calling them to our attention. And broken
ribs mean trouble, Dr. Ford, if the patient gets pneumonia,"

he monotoned. "Never miss a broken rib or bad bruises when you examine a patient just come in, Dr. Ford, and put them down in writing on the history sheet. It saves everybody a lot of trouble later on."

"I'll try not to slip up," answered Ford.

"And be careful when you tube-feed them—if they are unconscious be particularly sure the tube is in the gullet and not in the windpipe—and don't let any of the attendants get rough with them," he added as he moved back impassively toward his office.

Ford began to understand. It dawned on him that the problem of many, perhaps the majority of the mentally ill who had reached the stage requiring commitment to a hospital was really a matter of physical care and differed sharply from the acute problems treated in active university psychiatric clinics in a city such as Munich. Then it became apparent to him as he reflected that unimaginative, conscientious men such as Perkins contributed and were willing to contribute something of themselves to these "uninteresting" patients which more brilliant, scientifically-minded men somehow regarded as beneath them. The hopeless people were problems not to be dismissed lightly.

Gradually Ford settled down into the routine of the life of a closed institution. He became acquainted with the endless grumbling about "grub" and the rivalries which for most of the staff centered about a struggle for better living quarters; the conflicting ambitions for advancement in rank to the vacancies always occurring by the expansion and increases in the staffs in the vast state hospital system; the squabbling and scheming of the usually childless womenfolk of the doctors; the gossip about the changing degree of favor in which various men stood with their superiors; the rumors of strife and disagreement among these men in high authority.

It was a life of dreary repetition in many of its aspects but

it had no boredom for any physician who had the eyes to see,
the heart to feel and the mind to grasp the limitless variety
of symptoms related to him by patients, and the common as
well as rare examples of psychological illness which appeared
among the variously handicapped people for whom the struggle to exist in a realistic world had become too difficult and
had ended in mental derangement.

The yellow leaves of the maples lining the path to the
Admission Ward had begun to flutter down and carpet the
dark grey cinder walk. Looking toward the northeast end of
the grounds a long vista of stacked corn-stalks gave the impression of a quiet country cornfield.

Freud, bringing Jung of Zurich and Ferenczi of Budapest
with him, had come to America and gone back to Vienna
without making a great impression upon William James and
most of the other distinguished New Englanders who came to
hear him lecture at Worcester, curious to learn about the
new theories of psychoanalysis from their discoverer. And
America did not please Freud. The attempts to exploit and
rush him around annoyed him. He thought the American
mode of life too hurried, men worked too hard for wealth
alone, the food was bad.

To a few of the staff of Eastern the American visit of
the European psychoanalysts brought an increased interest
in the psychology of neuroses and dementia praecox. To Dr.
Perkins this increased interest meant not only new but pur-
poseless work, longer histories, more typewriting, more discussion at staff meetings without any apparent benefit to patients' welfare or doctors' efficiency. The time, he demurred,
could be better spent—if spent it must be—in the back wards
seeing to it that patients were not lost in the crowd and that
those who could be employed in the fields and gardens, in the
laundries and bakeries, in the carpenter shops and work-
rooms were urged and assisted to do so. "That would help

them more than any of this new fangled psychology," he muttered.

"Doctor Ford, would you examine Jock MacKaye," said Perkins one afternoon late in October, "seems to be a simple case of dementia praecox, hallucinating all the time."

Soon thereafter an attendant entered Ford's office with MacKaye, an under-sized, thin, narrow-chested man of about forty, with a long, hollow-cheeked, pimply face and a sparse growth of brown hair on his cheeks and chin. As he stood listlessly inside the doorway, looking aimlessly here and there, his jaw kept up a continuous chewing motion. Now and then he turned his head to one side or the other while a silly sort of grin came over his face.

"Sit down, won't you?" invited Ford with a nod toward a chair while he seated himself at a small table which acted as a desk.

MacKaye obeyed automatically and sat there holding his body rigidly, and his face blank, yet never ceasing the motions of his head, jaw and eyes while Ford reviewed the blue commitment blank from Bellevue. On it were many familiar phrases: "He is dull, uncommunicative and deteriorated;" "will not reply to questions;" "shows many stereotyped movements;" "reacts to auditory hallucinations;" "no evidence of alcohol at time of arrest or while under observation." As exceptional information on the form, Ford noticed that MacKaye had been "picked up by the police at Thirty-seventh Street and Second Avenue where he was acting peculiarly and gave no name of relatives".

The history form of patients in state hospitals called for a long list of facts and observations as to their general attitude, their "stream of mental activity", the results of intellectual tests for general knowledge and intelligence, ability to calculate and write, and a great many details about previous physical diseases and mental reactions. The main interest, however, was centered around current mental disorder and the diagnosis, for the latter indicated the probability of recovery or chronicity or, in some cases, predicted death in the near future.

Jock MacKaye did not help the examiner with his task. His replies came slowly, seldom more than a few words even after the physician had repeated the most simple questions over and over again. The unfamiliar Scottish burr did not make things easier for the examiner. Ford gathered that he had been an itinerant farm hand who had seldom stayed long at one place; that he had no friends; that he had married but did not know what had become of his wife.

After each answer MacKaye shook his head and his little pig-like eyes would glance slyly at the doctor. For what seemed minutes at a time he would cock his head to one side as if listening. Finally, unable to bring out the story of hallucinations by indirect questions and wearied by his patient's lack of cooperation, Ford in exasperation abandoned what he had been taught to be good interview technique and asked point-blank: "Do you hear voices?"

The little man again tilted his head, squinted and said with a pronounced burr, "Voices talk to me aw the time."

"And whose voices are they?"

"The bees and the birds, they talk to me."

"And what do they say?"

"They say 'be a guid lad, noo, Jock'; they sing and they buzz—'Jock, be a guid lad and Jesus will love ye.' "

"What else do they say?"

"That's aw."

"And for how long have they been saying it?"

"A lang time."

"How long?"

"A lang time. They're whispering richt noo," he said listening intently—" 'Dinna da nothing wrang. Take guid care of yeself. Jock, be a guid laddie'." He remained in an attitude of intent listening. His lips began to move silently, his head twisted to the right and the tiny pig-eyes were half-closed.

From this time on MacKaye would reply no more to Ford's questioning. He seemed contentedly absorbed in communicating with the birds and the bees. The examination had come to an abrupt and unsatisfactory end.

Each newly admitted patient to the hospital had to be presented by his examining physician at a conference to the other members of the staff for diagnosis and classification. These meetings were formal affairs, a sort of psychiatric tribunal, where the examining physician's findings and opinions were subject to questioning and criticism by the rest of the doctors—especially by those old-timer physicians who were likely to care for that patient later on when he was transferred from the Admission Ward to the chronic buildings.

Doctor Forrest, the solemn clinical director, presided at these conferences usually with a formality so unflagging and pretentious that at times it seemed slightly ridiculous. It was he who determined the label to be pasted on the patient's illness and this label in turn decided the patient's fate, at least for the time being. The chief, though inclined to bully the dawdlers of the staff, was himself vulnerable to counter-attack. At such times a deep crimson blush would slowly suffuse his face, overflow the unmarked boundary of his forehead and end in a broad flush on his shiny pate. He encouraged debate at these conferences, for one of his functions was to keep alive a scientific interest in the clinical aspects of the patient's illness. Many of the older resident physicians resented this modern method of approach so foreign to their way of thinking. Nevertheless, they all took sides in the lengthy discussions on diagnoses which most often centered around two forms of disease at times not easily distinguishable—dementia praecox and manic-depressive insanity. In the broadest term the former usually meant chronicity, the latter recoverability. These two diagnoses covered between sixty or seventy per cent of all the patients in the hospital.

After the staff had had their say, the chief would speak and then usually turn a question deliberately, a trifle maliciously, upon some somnolent doctor in the rear of the semi-circular group. "Doctor, do you think we are dealing with a case of dementia praecox or manic-depressive insanity?" and the drowsing man would arouse himself with a start and hastily blurt forth one term or the other.

The old-timers, such as Perkins, would be inclined to "praecox" and the long stay in the hospital which this diagnosis carried with it. The more optimistic younger men, among them the chief, would be likely to think in the more favorable light of manic-depressive. Partridge, eager to be classed with the scientifically minded, would follow the discussion intently hoping for clues from the chief as to how he would align himself when called upon to cast his vote for a diagnosis.

Ford read MacKaye's history aloud and the chief questioned the patient about indulgence in alcohol.

"How much do you drink, MacKaye?"

"A wee drap."

"And how much is that for a Scotchman?"

"A wee drap."

"The hallucinations have nothing of the threatening or the fearful in them that is characteristic of the alcoholic," stated Forrest pedantically, "on the other hand, their religious coloring is typical of dementia praecox." No one doubted the diagnosis. This was surely a text-book case of dementia praecox, everybody concurred.

At the end of three or four months, or earlier if the patient was considered ready for discharge, he was presented at a second staff conference when the previous diagnostic skill of the doctors would be shown to be correct or mistaken.

The heavy rain of a February storm beat against the grilled

windows of the gloomy staff meeting room when Dr. Howell, a dried and bony veteran who had spent thirty years on the back wards, brought MacKaye up for final disposition. The subsequent notes on his chart read, "still hallucinating actively—somewhat deteriorated—does a little work about the ward". Dr. Forrest questioned MacKaye briefly as the small Scotchman kept his head cocked to one side.

"Yes, Ay hear voices aw the time—the birds singin' and the bees abuzzin'."

"But there are no birds and bees about on a cold, winter day like this—what do they say?" interrogated Forrest in his serious manner.

"They say, 'Jock, ye're guid lad—take care o' Jock'."

An attendant led him back to a chronic ward. His fate had been sealed. For the rest of his days the State of New York would provide an iron cot in a long row of iron cots in a stale smelling corridor-like ward, coarse clothing and plain but hearty food for Jock MacKaye. He might live that way for another thirty years.

An old clump of forsythia with its cane-like stalks had blossomed into a pale yellow at one corner of the Admission Building and a few of its bell-like flowers lay strewn around the base of the clump. The maples had budded into tender, fresh green leaves, the wide bed of tulips along the road to the main building were showing white, purple and pink petals. Within the grim Admission Ward it was staff meeting day and a conference was going on. Patients ready for discharge into an unsympathetic outside world were brought before the medical court. They were mostly people whose excitements or depressions had automatically burned themselves out, or those who had taken too much alcohol and whose minds had now cleared up under abstinence, rest and routine care, or impulsive, reckless psychopaths who had quieted down under a similar regime and were ready to be turned loose to face an intolerant community. Toward the end of the meeting the desiccated Dr. Howell said to the chief: "There's a case which I would like to present for discharge. His name is MacKaye."

A semblance of a smile cracked the parched skin of Howell's face and the tremor of his hand became more marked as he had the thin man ushered in.

"This patient was presented at the staff meeting last February and unanimously diagnosed as dementia praecox," he said, stressing the "unanimous" with a slight note of exultation in his voice. It did not displease him that the chief appeared surprised and disturbed at the unexpected turn in the case. The tell-tale blush began to mount the latter's cheeks and showed a little above his bushy, red eyebrows for Dr. Forrest prided himself, above all other things, on his ability to diagnose dementia praecox.

"How does this happen?" he said in a challenging voice.

"He's recovered," asserted Dr. Howell positively and with an implied triumph which made the rest of the assembled staff take notice. "He has been working with the gardener regularly for a month, he is quiet, helpful and well behaved on the ward. He has complete insight. All his hallucinations have disappeared."

Dr. Forrest looked very red and aggrieved. He had been glancing over MacKaye's chart with its original examination notes made by Ford six months before and the opinions expressed at the first and second staff meetings, including his own definitely on the record. With evident annoyance he turned to the waiting patient who regarded him calmly.

"What about those voices—the birds and bees, MacKaye," he asked sharply, almost intimidatingly.

"I donna hear them any more," replied the patient laconically shaking his head, entirely unperturbed.

"And how long ago did they stop?" Forrest continued incredulously.

"About a month, noo, mon."

"And why do you think that happened?"

"They aye stop in April," replied MacKaye with bland unconcern.

"And what do you mean by that", pursued Forrest thoroughly irritated. The uncontrollable blush now covered his crown with a scarlet cap of error.

"Well, ye ken, Doctor, they aye starts in the autumn when the could weather comes along and stop in the spring."

"A most unusual symptom", commented Forrest sarcastically. "Tell us more about it."

"Well, it's like this way, Doctor," he said suddenly becoming loquacious. "When the could comes, I starts to hear the voices and they say, 'Jock, noo, it's time to take care of yaursel'. And I listen to them on the street and talk back to them. And then a crowd gathers 'round me, police come and a cop takes me to the police office and the police look daft and send me to the loonie ward. And then they examine me and then they always send me up to a nice warm place and I get well taken care of—just like the bees tell me. But when the sun starts to shine warm in the spring and the birds start achirpin', the voices aye stop and I say to myself, 'Jock, noos the time to move on'. Every year it's aye the same." He looked up and squinted cannily at a subdued Dr. Forrest.

"Ye've got a grand hospital doun here, Doctor," he said with respectful deliberation. "And Doctor Howell is a grand mon but I liked Danvers up in Massachusetts State better— and Middletown, up in Connecticut, is aw'recht, too." He paused, tilted his head a little and said simply as an afterthought, "Ay, an ye can save a wee bit o' money, too." Dr. Forrest looked discomfited. One or two of the staff snickered furtively.

"This is obviously a case of malingering," said Forrest ponderously, seeking to retrieve himself in a display of erudition. "But it is evident that the man is not quite normal. It is my opinion," he continued weightily, "that malingering in itself is always an evidence of abnormality. Therefore we can reclassify his case as one of constitutional psychopathic personality. We will discharge him as such. I see you made the original examination, Dr. Ford," he commented stiffly, regaining his composure and normal coloring.

"Yes, sir," answered Ford, quite as ashamed of his own failure to detect the sham originally as Forrest had been later. He found some solace in the thought that the patient had often fooled far more experienced doctors and this time even the seasoned men at Bellevue. He wondered too if the wily patient had become assured from his previous experience, that the vanity of the physicians would allow him to escape unpunished. They would not want to expose their fallibility.

"You should have been more careful, Dr. Ford, and investigated the hallucinations to find any psychological elements of wish fulfillment which Bleuler has discovered often to be present in the content of the hallucination. These are similar to the wish-fulfilling function which Freud has pointed out in dreams."

"Pop" Perkins chuckled perceptibly. As he and Ford later walked back to the Reception Ward he drawled, "Guess it was fulfillment of a wish. That Jock MacKaye sure did fool you and me too, Benny, but I wouldn't take fifty dollars for the way he fooled Forrest—board and lodging for the stormy months. You know he reminds me of a ship's doctor from the Atlas Line—the one that runs down to the Caribbean. Laziest son of a sea cook and biggest grafter that I ever saw. He came on the staff here one June and left in October—told me confidentially he always did the same thing every year. He took a job at a different state hospital late every spring and stayed for about six months. He never had any trouble getting in either, just like MacKaye, only he didn't like cruising in the tropics in the summer time."

Perkins peered over his glasses. Then he took them off, chewed at the end of a shaft for a moment, and began talking to Ford with unwonted freedom.

"Remember the old biddy I showed you the first day you came here, Benny, the one who kept yelling about the jobs the patients made for us? Board and lodging. Just like this Jock fellow, some of us doctors here at Eastern are too, I suppose. But then maybe it's only old fellows like Howell and me and a few of the other unscientific fogies around here who feel the need of having a place where we know we're safe and warm and three meals a day. It's one way of getting through. I guess that's why we understand some of the people on the back wards better than Forrest does or some of these reformers and muck-rakers always ranting about the conditions in insane hospitals but who wouldn't take a job in one for two days."

After his revealing outburst Perkins lapsed into his usual colorless drawl. "Dr. Ford," he said, "I noticed before we went to staff meeting that the colored man in the bed with sideboards on the right hand side of the ward is exhausting himself with his tossing about—would you see to it that he does not hurt himself—and give him two eggs, a pint of milk and a little whisky through a stomach tube. And let him have a small hypo of morphine, a quarter of a grain. Repeat it in two hours if he doesn't quiet down. Do it yourself, will you. He's a little too restless to trust it to any of the nurses."

IV

THROUGH FOREVER

A warm midday May sun shone down brightly upon an almost empty street on the upper West side of New York. A shaggy horse, drawing an old green wagon full of bright geraniums, hydrangeas and pansies, clopped along as the vendor walking beside his colorful wares looked towards opened windows hopefully. Nothing in the calm scene to recall the thought of war or tragedy: yet only the day before the news of the sinking of the Lusitania had been flashed across the sea, across the continent, throwing an entire tense nation into a state of indignation and quickening the fear of war with Germany and Austria.

Down the quiet street, past the neatly-kept brownstone houses, a woman and a man walked hesitatingly. The woman, sandy-haired, tall and heavily built, was dressed in a black and white flower-printed dress which hung loosely upon her ample, sagging figure. The man, short and stoutish, wore a light checked grey suit too tight for his bulging middle-aged figure, and a straight-brimmed, soiled, yellow straw hat. Nothing in their aspect suggested the torments of love or trouble unless, perhaps, the uncertain way in which they proceeded and scanned the house numbers. A close observer might have noted that although walking together a space always remained between them whichever way they moved. They peered independently at the numbers and stopped at last before one where a small, black-lettered, brass sign was placed in a window at street level. It read:

BENJAMIN FORD, M.D.

82

The couple stood for a while looking at it. Then, without speaking they walked on, hesitated again, retraced their steps and went up the stoop of the house with the doctor's sign. The woman rang the bell gingerly. A gawky Irish maid in black dress with a white cap and apron answered the ring and showed them into the waiting room at the right of the entrance hall. Then she knocked at the door of the doctor's office in the rear.

"Dochter, there's some funny looking people that sez they want to see you—sez their names is Warner—sez Dochter Nasmyth sint thim. Will ye be wantin' to see thim?"

The maid was a raw-boned, frank-looking, friendly girl, not too long ago come through the port of Cork—a type of servant already rapidly disappearing from the New York domestic scene. She had been in service with the doctor for several years. While the office without surgical instruments or a cabinet for medicines and the long sessions with each person puzzled her, she did not question the doctor's ability or the quality of his practice. She knew that most of his patients came time after time and each stayed an hour and that the large arm-chair in front of his desk in which they sat was becoming rapidly worn. She loyally protected him from unappointed intruders.

Dr. Ford was preparing to leave for lunch. He looked at the flat, oval clock on his desk. The fact that Nasmyth had referred them made him decide to see the newcomers.

"It's all right, Delia, I'll see them," he nodded to her and she opened the folding doors which separated the waiting room from the large office.

"Won't you come in," he said to the waiting couple.

As they rose diffidently and walked self-consciously into the office, Dr. Ford sized them up. What united this pair? Which of the two was the afflicted one? The fact that two people came together for a first visit usually meant they were joined by a mutual responsibility. Sometimes they were husband and wife, at others, brother and sister, parent and son or daughter. These two did not seem to fit into any of the categories.

"Won't you be seated, Mrs. Warner", said Ford.

"I'm not Mrs. Warner", replied the woman with some irritation in her voice. "I'm Mrs. Bentley. He is Mr. Warner. Mr. Hoibert Warner."

She took a seat in a deep arm-chair near the doctor's desk. Mr. Warner who had followed the fleshy woman stood behind her dejectedly but said nothing and followed her example by sitting down uneasily on a straight-backed chair further away. He seemed at a loss what to do with his hands —first put them in the pockets of the drab grey coat he wore, then allowed them to dangle limply at his side and finally automatically clasped them across his round little paunch. This seemed to satisfy him and he settled down into an attitude of passive defense. Neither of the visitors spoke for a while.

Dr. Ford took his accustomed place in a swivel chair behind his desk and observed the oddly matched aloof couple for a minute or two. He was not quite certain who was the patient.

"What seems to be the trouble?" he asked without addressing either one of them specifically.

"Dr. Nasmyth told us to come to you", replied Mrs. Bentley in a flat, nasal tone. "He took care of my boy when he had pus on his chest and had to take out three ribs."

Ford thought of the perfect spring day outside and wondered how long he was going to be held here listening to the woman's irrelevant remarks.

"Yes, Nasmyth's a truly great surgeon. How did you happen to go to him now?"

"A wonderful man. But he couldn't do anything for me. He said my trouble wuzn't in his line. He said we should see you and gave me this note."

She produced from a bulging, soiled, yellow cloth hand-bag a somewhat crumpled sealed envelope addressed to Dr. Ford. Dated nearly a fortnight before it read:

"Dear Benny:

I'm wishing these on you. I don't know whether she is crazy or he's crazy or they're both crazy. But I guess that's your job, so don't blame me—serves you right for being sucked into such a game.

Smitty."

"What is your trouble?" pursued Ford looking up from the note at Mrs. Bentley with a smile.

"It's my ear, Doctor, my right ear! There's a thumping and roaring in it all the time. Funny, for I'm deaf on that side. It's driving me crazy! I can't stand it any longer!"

"Have you consulted an ear specialist?" asked Ford sympathetically.

"Yes. The ear doctor at the New York Dispensary. He said it wuz noives."

"How long has it been going on?"

"For two years now. It keeps me awake nights."

"You find no relief from it?"

"In the daytime I walk the streets under the elevated trains. The noise of the trains drowns out the noises in my ear."

The woman gazed straight ahead with dulled, weary-looking hazel eyes. The lines in her face sagged, the corners of her mouth dropped as if set for eternity in dejection.

"And how did it begin?" probed the doctor.

A long pause. Finally, in a tired, dry voice Mrs. Bentley spoke.

"Dr. Nasmyth said I must tell you everything or I won't get well."

"I think that telling all the truth may help you to get well."

"Then—here's the truth", she said, looking over her shoulder at the still silent Mr. Warner who sat like a watery-eyed billiken hugging his round little paunch. "I've been wicked", she said. "I've been very wicked. I've been wicked with Hoibert, there."

The co-partner in sin shifted furtively and glanced toward the door. His faded blue eyes blurred with tears as he repressed his evident urge to slip away but he said nothing.

Dr. Ford waited several minutes before he asked, "What happened?"

"He gave me a terrible disease. I didn't know what it wuz. I had a cold in my nose. It lasted for months and never seemed to get well. I went to Dr. Nasmyth. I used to live in Cooperstown—that wuz when I was married to Mr. Bentley. We knew Dr. Nasmyth's folks up there right well. Everybody said he'd be a great man some day."

"And Dr. Nasmyth sent you to the nose doctor", said Ford, picking up the thread of thought for her.

"Yes, and the nose doctor thought I wuz Dr. Nasmyth's patient and called him up and told him it wuz that terrible disease. Syphilis," she added, speaking the awful word fearfully. "I wuz so ashamed that anyone from home should know!" And Mrs. Bentley bowed her head, weeping silently.

The unspeakable disease! The disease which at that time many people still thought incurable or could be helped only by long and painful courses of mercury and iodide; the disease which was associated almost exclusively at that time with "sin" and extra-marital relations. The word could not be spoken in polite society or printed in ordinary books.

The doctor looked attentively at Mrs. Bentley, noting the slightly sunken bridge of the nose which accounted for the peculiar flatness of her face, betraying the final stage of syphilis when vital nerves are damaged and bones threatened with destruction. He glanced then at Mr. Warner who merely blinked his red-rimmed lids in an embarrassed way and pressed his crossed pudgy hands spasmodically into his belly.

"Did the ear doctor think your deafness was caused by the other disease?" asked Ford kindly.

"Yes, he said that but he said, too, that the noises might be due to noivousness. He said I wuz very noivous and that made everything worse. I suppose that's why Dr. Nasmyth sent me to you. You're a noive doctor, aren't you?"

"Yes, at least I know about nerves," said Ford, "and that being anxious about something makes the pain in any part of the body more severe. You can't help but watch the suffering part all the time. People with stomach or heart trouble complain of this aggravation of pain whenever they are worried," explained the doctor. "Is Cooperstown your home?"

"No. We—Hoibert and I—were raised in Fordham. We went to the same school up there."

"And how long ago was that?"

"About twenty-five years ago", replied Mrs. Bentley simpering. "I wuz just a young girl then." She smoothed the printed skirt complacently over her enormous thighs.

"Thoity years ago!" blurted out Mr. Warner opening his mouth for the first time. "Thoity—not twenty-five!" The fearful, grayish man spoke confidently; at last he could relinquish his defensive position, affirm something which he felt could not be contradicted.

"Twenty-five or maybe twenty-seven at the most, Doctor," insisted Mrs. Bentley. "Don't listen to him!"

"I say thoity! I know how old I am even if you try damn hard to forget how old you are! I show the facts," snapped Warner, now belligerent.

"You see how he is, Doctor? Always arguing!" said Mrs. Bentley, her flat voice taking on a slight edge.

"How about yerself? Always exaggerating. I says it's no use, she can't enjoy nothing," retorted Warner angrily, his red eyelids becoming redder than ever.

"I never can talk anything with him, Doctor! It always ends in a fight."

Mrs. Bentley was flopping about in her chair like a large seal. It now became apparent to Ford that the ear and even the dread syphilis were of secondary importance. He wondered how long this scene of conjugal—extra-conjugal—felicity was going to continue. Outside the spring day beckoned and he cussed Smitty for having referred the quarrelsome couple, but nothing in his manner revealed any impatience he might feel.

"What does it matter?" he interposed calmly. "Each of us shows our age in a different and particular way, in some part of the body and nature seldom conceals it. It's of no importance to your case. How long has Mr. Bentley been dead?"

Again Mrs. Bentley sighed, lowered her eyes, hung her head.

"It's like going to confession in choich," she muttered automatically. "Must I tell you everything, Doctor? Do I have to tell you everything—like Dr. Nasmyth said or I won't get well?"

"Yes," said Ford. "But I am neither priest nor judge. I am here only to help you if I can."

"Well, then—I've been wicked. I've been very wicked. Mr. Bentley's not dead. I'm divorced."

Divorce in that day was still an unacceptable, unrespectable state especially for women. The doctor remained serene:

"And how long ago was that?"

"Oh, about five years ago. My husband wuz a terrible man. He wuz drunk and arguing all the time. When he wuz drunk he beat me if I crossed him. We were always having rows,

So I got a divorce." Mrs. Bentley cast her eyes heavenward, then lowered her lashes again piously.

"But I've been wicked," she said in a flat monotone. "We got a divorce by collusion. I caught my husband in a hotel in Utica. He told us where to find him."

She sat up stiffly, gazing fixedly at the ceiling. Mr. Warner relaxed the pressure on his paunch and his lips twitched in a self-satisfied smirk.

"Then I came back home with the children to my mother's in Fordham. She still had our little house there. I had to work and so I got a job at Schrafft's as head waitress. And only about two weeks after I began work who should I run into but Hoibert on the 'L' station." She tittered slightly, glancing kittenishly at Warner who hung his head abashed. "We were certainly glad to meet up with each other again," she added simpering, "wasn't we, Hoibert?"

"Did you meet frequently after that?"

"Oh, yes. We began going together steady. You know how it is, Doctor," the woman said with awkward coquettishness.

"Who egged me on? You did!" pouted Warner accusingly. "I wuz living with my mother, taking care of her—gave her twenty dollars every week. It was better, living with my mom. And she warned me against you! I wish I had listened to her!"

The bickering threatened to be renewed. Ford intervened decisively.

"How long was it after you began your association that the disease appeared?"

"About two years," replied Mrs. Bentley.

"Did you know you had the disease?" asked Ford turning from her directly to the man.

"I thought I wuz cured," protested Warner. "I took treatment from a doctor in Brooklyn for four months. He gave me twelve shots of that new German medicine. Injections into the blood. There wuzn't a sign of it on me!"

"But were you pronounced definitely cured by your doctor?"

"Well, he took a blood test. Said it wuzn't quite poifect. But doctors like to keep you running. And he charged me twenty dollars a shot."

"Did you tell Mrs. Bentley here about it?"

"Yeh, I sure did. She said she didn't care. Didn't you?" The little man's doughy face was inflamed now with anger.

"You told me you wuz cured. You know you did, Hoibert."

"I didn't and you know it." The gray, saggy man glared at her. Yet, at the same time, he seemed to be secretly glad of her participation in the responsibility.

"You know you didn't tell me how bad it wuz! You see, Doctor, how he is always arguing? I can't get anywhere with him. His mother spoils him!" She was all virtue, appealing to Ford for approval but he ignored the plea.

"And did you keep on with him after you learned of your trouble, Mrs. Bentley?"

"Yes, she did! She's a hot baby", cried Warner viciously, turning in rage upon the woman. "She said she didn't care what happened. You wuz the one who didn't want to stop! What for am I knocking myself out?"

The woman flushed with shame but said meekly, "But Hoibert, everybody knew we wuz going together and everybody thought we wuz going to be married."

"You mean you thought so and a lot of old women," snorted Warner. "Stop squawking."

"You talked about it a lot, too," protested Mrs. Bentley mildly. Suddenly her manner changed. "I just can't stand this anymore, Doctor", and her flat voice took on a shrill note. "My ear is thumping like mad now. It's bad enough all the time but when I get excited I just can't stand it."

She rose from her chair and began walking agitatedly about the room. Then she resumed her seat in the arm-chair and pressed her fingers deep into the right side of her neck.

"That helps some," she said, "stops the thumping but not the roaring. I found that out by myself."

"You have closed off the arteries to the ear by pressure in that way," explained the doctor. "Has nothing been able to help your ear noises?"

"Nothing but the noise of the elevated train—it drowns it out. It roars like a power house—but by now I'm getting used to living in the power house. I could stand it somehow if I didn't have this other trouble with Hoibert. That's getting woise all the time."

"And why so just now?" inquired Ford.

"It's my boy, Billy. He's fourteen now and he's getting awful wise. He's sorta jealous of Hoibsie. The thing just ain't right. It would be different if we wuz married."

"He's just a damn fresh kid. Too big for his pants—oughta be spanked," spouted Warner. "She is always bringing up dese mean issues which we only scratch the surface of."

"I do not know that your marriage to Mr. Warner would necessarily change that particular phase of the situation", said Ford. "You know often a certain jealousy exists between growing sons and their own fathers—to say nothing of stepfathers."

"Me step-daddy to that snoot Billy. It's a dead give-away what you're after. Can you see me? I never said I would marry you!" He turned to the woman a face defiant with self-interest. "Not even after you got it. Much less before!"

"What difference does it make what you said. You gave it to me! Now will you marry me?" Mrs. Bentley threw out the words with finality.

Warner looked imploringly at Ford, then glanced at Mrs. Bentley timorously. Small beads of perspiration glistened on his pasty forehead and his pale blue eyes bulged. Dr. Ford regarded the two impassively as they glowered at each other, Warner visibly cringing under the sustained gaze of Mrs. Bentley's white-lashed, hazel eyes.

"Well, all right then—I'll marry you!" said Warner after a long pause in a small, faltering voice.

Mrs. Bentley's eyes began to show fire. She rose from her chair and walked over to where Warner sat.

"This is the last straw," she exploded. "I've followed you around like a monkey—now I'm through with you forever! By God, I wouldn't marry you."

She drew back her right arm full length, swung it around and let all the force of the swing end in a stinging slap across Warner's cheek. Then she swept out of the doctor's office. Ford thought that the dowdy woman had assumed a certain dignity, a momentary majesty in her indignation. The outer door closed with a bang.

Mr. Warner slumped in his chair, hanging his head in disgrace. The reddened left cheek contrasted markedly with the doughy whiteness of the right. Then he rose slowly on shaky legs.

"That's a woman for you, Doctor, always squalling and squawking and born with jealousy in the blood. I says to myself it's no use. Mom's right. Mom's always been against her. But, then, Mom don't know all there is to know about me, neither," he said, looking slyly about the room as though Mom might be lurking in some obscure corner. "Well, Doctor, it looks as if I am well rid of her, don't it?"

He fumbled in his coat pockets, embarrassed.

"Do we owe you anything for this visit, Doctor?"

"As you wish," said Dr. Ford glad to have the interview end.

"I . . . I guess I left my hat in the other room", said Mr. Warner visibly relieved. And, opening the folding doors slightly he squeezed through as imperceptibly as possible and tip-toed quietly away.

As Dr. Ford washed up over a basin before going for the long postponed lunch, the drama of the final scene reappeared vividly in his mind. The shallow, sensuous woman had shown more courage and independence than he had credited her. Then he became annoyed with himself. They had both gotten off cheap, the "cheap" couple, he thought. Maybe once again he'd been too lenient in letting that little man leave without paying at least a token fee. He'd charge it up to Smitty and profit and loss.

But Ford's mood changed immediately and he smiled. The past hour had given him one more slant on the limitless vagaries of human nature; another glimpse, too, into the morass of trouble and disease into which people are plunged. He reflected for a moment: how much remained still to be discovered in the enigmas of humans notwithstanding the contributions of Freud and his followers in Europe as well as here. The medical schools were slow to accept the implications of the new psychology for the help and understanding physical illness. Only a few weeks ago he had been given a hint by the dean—or was it a warning—that "psychoanalysis had no place in an undergraduate medical school".

Ford hurried out to pick up a bite at the corner drug store before going to Bellevue for teaching rounds. The work there had become heavier recently. The war's impact on the doctor's duties was already making itself felt, for the Canadians and some others of the teaching staff had left to serve with the British Medical Corps, badly in need of physicians.

As he approached the corner where the side street crossed the avenue he spied a tall, fleshy woman in a black flowered dress engaged in earnest conversation with a pudgy man wearing a yellowish, last year's straw hat. The woman, bending toward the man, was talking so vigorously that she might have been scolding. The pudgy man stood so close to her that his round paunch seemed to support her sagging abdomen as he talked back with a defiant upward toss of his head. The woman, looking down the street toward the river may have spied Dr. Ford. He was not sure. Then a trolley car which had come bouncing and swaying down the avenue halted just before the quarreling couple. They hurriedly crossed the street to board it. The pudgy man helped the heavy woman up the high step of the car, clumsily yet solicitously, and then followed her in.

Ford watched the car as it vanished down the sunny street along the glistening trolley tracks. He chuckled and as he shook his head, said half aloud, "Through forever! Glued forever! That's more like it."

V

THE WILL

The patient lifted himself from the worn, brown leather couch and slouched towards the door of Dr. Ford's office high over Gramercy Park. He did not bother to say good-night as he went into the hall leaving the door partly open. The doctor remained seated in the broad arm-chair at the head of the couch. For several years he had been using this method first advocated by Freud of allowing patients to unburden themselves in a recumbent, relaxed position, facing away from the listening physician. Freud, here, had combined the ideas inherent in a treatment session with a mesmerist and the secrecy of the confessional. Ford had found that Freud's theory and method worked well in practice because both the doctor and the patient profited from the partial anonymity thus created between them.

Today Ford was weary and just a bit discouraged, too. He was quite ready for an evening off in the company of his old friend, Dr. Nasmyth, who had promised to take him to see the heavyweight championship fight between young Jack Dempsey and an unknown South American giant, Luis Firpo. Yes, it would be a welcome break in his deadening routine. How that last patient had rambled and droned on drearily during his hour, repeating things he'd said dozens of times before. The day had been a frightfully hot one for September. Well, thank heaven, the man was gone now, no matter how unceremoniously. Ford allowed himself to sag, closed his eyes and fell into a half-sleep.

"Hello there, Benny," said Smitty cheerfully, entering the

room. "Not dozing in your chair like an old man, are you? Well, you're forgiven. The day is a scorcher." He subsided informally into an arm-chair. Nasmyth, freshly shaven and jaunty in a crisp, white linen suit, was still not the young Smitty of bygone days. The strain through the years of his long hours in the operating room was beginning to show in the gray streaks of his thinning hair and in the deepening furrows of the forehead.

"I'll confess, Smitty, I damned near fell asleep during office hours this afternoon. Right while the patients were here, on the couch, telling me all about themselves!"

"The point is, did you?"

"No, I managed not to, but Richard Mayfield, ever hear of him?—says it happened to him in an amusing way. He's one of the really good analysts up in Boston. I've spoken to you of him before. Anyway, Dick was sitting behind a patient who talked on and on monotonously and he simply fell sound asleep. But unfortunately, or maybe fortunately, the patient wore a wrist-watch, checked up on the hour and discovered the doctor snoozing peacefully. So he rose quietly, shook his sleeping doctor gently by the shoulders and said, 'Wake up, Doctor, the hour is over. I'll send you my bill'."

"Hope he collected," chuckled Smitty. "I'll bet that ended the treatments with that patient."

"Not at all. The fellow said he didn't blame Dick a bit for being put to sleep by all his drivel!"

"Good idea you fellows have, squatting down behind those poor devils so they can't see what you're doing. But are you sure Dick isn't just a nom de plume for Benny?"

"Not this time! But I could hardly keep my eyes open with this last man. Tired as all hell. But the muggy day and eight dull hours with patients aren't the only reasons for my being hot and disgusted just now," said Ford with a tinge of bitterness. "You know, Smitty, I heard just this morning that Hamilton Hooker had been appointed the associate professor

in psychiatry down at the Medical School. I have rather suspected for some time it might happen—too many of the die-
hards don't like psychoanalysis. I guess I may as well resign."

"Well, I'll be damned," exploded Smitty, puffing quickly
at his cigarette in indignant partisanship, "Ham Hooker
never had an idea of his own in his noodle. Nice enough
fellow but just a conscientious routinist."

"I guess that's the kind of man they want. Someone who
fits in and won't cause trouble by stirring 'em up," agreed
Ford, comforted by his friend's understanding.

"But why in hell should you care?" continued Smitty,
"You don't need the job, spending all that time repeating the
same lecture and quizzes two or three times a year to new
crops of students. Now maybe you'll do some real writing.
You know though I'm always kidding you I believe you fellows have really got something. By the way, who was that
man I passed just now as I came in? The one with the awful
stoop and sagging shoulders. You ought to send him to a
good orthopedist to have that bend in his spine straightened
out instead of meddling with his complexes."

"You wouldn't believe it, old blood and pus, but it took
twenty-five years to develop that stoop," replied Ford. "And
it can't be straightened by a plaster cast or steel braces.
There's a story behind it."

"Another one of your case stories? Well, I'll survive. But
first fortify me with a good long strong drink of Scotch,
Benny."

Ford rose to prepare the drinks. Over the tinkling ice in
the glasses, his voice sounded from the adjoining room. "It's
good, this story, Smitty. We'll call him Frank Calucci, that's
near enough for you. In spite of that stoop of his, you may
have noticed he's quite a husky fellow. Well, that crooked
back of his reflects a fear. He's obsessed with the fear that at
any moment someone may steal up from behind and sur-
reptitiously strike him over the back of his head."

Dr. Ford appeared from the next room with the glasses. Smitty had taken off his coat and after a long sip leaned back in his chair.

"Well, go on. Whom does he fear? Who does he think might take a rap at him, and why, Professor?"

Ford subsided lazily into a comfortable slip-covered chair.

"Deep down in his unconscious he still fears the people of whom he originally stood in awe—his father and his older brother, Jerry. In addition, he suffers now from a fear that he will not be accepted by his acquaintances and will be rebuffed by his friends. His father is a tough old reprobate who began life with a junk handcart which in due course, gave way to a wobbly wagon pulled by a dejected, round-bellied old horse. Then a junk yard was acquired and finally he became the president of one of the leading scrap iron and metal companies, a real power in his trade."

"A rags-to-riches, Horatio Alger saga, typically American," commented Smitty. "But I'm still not impressed. What has that to do with those stooped shoulders of—what's his name?"

"Let's call him Frank Calucci," replied the doctor. "And that's his habitual gait and posture, with his head in a position of always being ready to duck. We have traced it back to the time when Tony, that's his father, caught him stealing at the age of seven and cuffed him over the back of his head. Mentally Frank has been dodging the old man's anger and blows ever since. Now, Smitty, do you see why those steel braces of yours won't change his stoop or him? You ought to know you can't give a man courage to stand on his own feet and relieve his inward quaking by operating and straightening out the bowed bones of his legs."

"Oh, I suppose you analysts catch them coming and going, from their nose to their toes. Have it your way, Benny. Just now I'm far more interested in my own gastronomic reactions to a first rate steak before the fight," said Smitty, picking up his hat. "Let's go around the square to Luchow's."

The following day Frank Calucci came on his customary visit to Dr. Ford. He was a short man whose curly black hair had begun to gray perceptibly above the temples and whose eyes shifted constantly from side to side as though on guard against invisible threats. His gruff manner and explosive voice masked a deep-seated timidity. Even before he took his accustomed place upon the couch, with his face turned away from Ford, he said, "A very funny thing has happened, Doc, and I don't know what to do about it. What do you think?"

"Well, I'm apt not to say much of what I think about a great many things which come up with my patients as you surely must have learned over this last year and a half," replied Ford. "But what's on your mind?"

A brief smile came over the face of Calucci immediately followed by a puzzled, anxious look.

"Are you ready for a big laugh? It's a funny thing, Doc. A couple of days ago I found out that the old man is gypping us—stealing from the firm. I kinda suspected it for a long time. I guess Pop's up to his old tricks."

Calucci lay silent on the couch for many minutes breathing deeply, his hands clasped behind his head and his legs firmly crossed. He was so quiet and immobile that the doctor thought at first he had gone to sleep. Previously Frank had sometimes lapsed into the escape of slumber when topics came up in the conversation about which he did not like to talk. But this time he lay in a silent reverie with reflections in his mind which Ford surmised, in view of the revelation just made, concerned his father, Tony, still fairly sturdy at sixty-five, his hands hard and horny although twenty years had passed since he had rummaged in backyards, alleyways and fields for old iron and bought cast-off copper pots and lead pipes. Finally the patient spoke.

"You remember how I told you he would steal junk when I used to ride around with him on the seat of that old wagon when I was a little shaver. Thought I didn't notice it, damn him. I can see him right now slipping into some backyard and sidling out with an old cast-iron stove, or bicycle frame, or a rusty bathtub. He was a pretty slick one, I'll say he was."

"But you have said yourself that your father bought much of his junk," interrupted Dr. Ford.

"Sure he did—when he had to! And you can bet he could drive a hard bargain then, if the kind I saw him put over when he got old and softened up a little means anything," retorted the younger Calucci.

When he became silent, Ford was sure that the patient had again reverted to childhood memories, thinking of the wagon and the weary horse which moved forward under Tony's authoritative "Gee" and the leather strip of a whip. At the front of the wagon a barrel stave had been nailed upright to each side and between them was stretched a piece of dirty, frayed clothes-line. From this line hung four bells of varied size which jangled inharmoniously as the wagon bumped slowly over the rough dirt roads about Corona, Long Island. It was then only a dingy settlement on the fringe of the irrepressible great city which was leaping from its island confines over the swift river to the flat, barren stretches of the huge island to the east.

Ford relit his cigar and sat quietly, patiently waiting.

Now Calucci spoke again, this time without rancor and almost with a tinge of admiration in his voice.

"Yes, Pop could spot scrap as quick as a gull sees a morsel of food on the top of the river. And was he sharp when it came to fixin' the price, and did he know how to handle the women in their wrappers when they tried to bargain with him through a half-open kitchen door. Every once in a while he used to slip inside the house, stay for five or ten minutes and come out lookin' sheepish. I was only a kid but I was on to him even then. It wasn't fair to Mom. She was all right, Mom was. She helped me out every time she could."

"But you have told me that you yourself are not treating your mother any too well even now that you are married and have two fine boys," commented Ford.

"I never could love anybody, Doc. But you remember the time when the old man beat me up, don't you, Mom couldn't do anything just that minute. She was too afraid of him. But when I ran and hid under her chair after he stomped out of the house, she took me on her lap in the rockin' chair and hugged me a little and just said, 'My Lulu'—and I knew everything was hunky-dory with her. The old man was tough, all right, with the women and in business. And I don't believe he ever made a square deal in all his life."

"His younger son appears to have been considerably influenced by his father's knack and example with the ladies, and also by his methods of doing business," interposed Ford dryly.

"I guess you're right there, Doc," agreed the patient with some pride. "But after all, Pop wasn't so bad. Before he finished up any trade, the old man would sight some stray salvage about the place and never miss a chance to include this extra junk in the transaction without asking any questions. Then he would come out to the wagon with the stuff he had bought, dump it on the floor and go back into the yard for those extra things. I couldn't help knowing it wasn't on the level by the way he would jump on his seat and whip up the old nag into a run, usually with the house owner's mutt yelping at our wheels."

Again Calucci ceased talking. Dr. Ford knew the episodes of his patient's childhood minutely, and reviewed them in his mind during the interval of silence.

Ford recalled how one day when Frank had just turned seven and was wandering around alone he spotted a gleaming frying-pan and a bright copper pot resting on the ledge of a kitchen back porch. A stealthy crawl, a quick flash of his arm and a scamper brought him and his booty beyond the range of capture. He carried the utensils home and concealed them, not too well, among a miscellany of dirty, rusting articles in one of his father's piles at the side of the house. He intended to sell them the next day to a rival junkman, who lived a few blocks away.

By chance, old Calucci decided the very next morning to load his wagon for a selling trip to the big wholesaler's scrap-metal yard off a siding of the railroad. A glint from the bright pan as he tossed the dull, black remnants of former implements into the wagon attracted his attention. He hurried with intuitive directness into the house. Finally he forced from Frank a confession of stealing them.

"Why 'a you steal? I teacha you not ta," bellowed Tony, his face dark with rage as he cuffed the terrified child over the back of the head and followed him as he tried to escape outdoors with a blow here, a slap there.

"I see you swipe stuff yourself," blurted the little boy with the candor of a child, but quite ignorant of the fact that what may be regarded as ethically proper for parents is quite intolerable to them in their children. His brother, Jerry, four years older, standing stiffly against the wall, viewed Frank's punishment with malicious satisfaction.

Then the doctor recalled another determinant happening in the patient's life—something for which the latter had no responsibility whatsoever.

Frank's father and mother, Tony and Annetta, had been married for six years when Frank came. It had not taken Annetta long to learn that the way to be sure of Tony was to obey him. For her, this had not been difficult. She had seen this pattern of life in her mother; she had read the pattern on her marriage day when she received from her grandmother in Italy as a wedding present a large, coarse linen tablecloth with a motto embroidered in red. It said, "Wife, do not annoy your husband."

Frank had been Annetta's child of affection. The first born, Jerry, had been a duty; the second, Tessie, had been something to love, something which even hard-hearted Tony seemed to love. But she had gone away soon in a small, white hearse drawn by two white horses in front of which walked five men in blue military suits dolefully blaring Chopin's Funeral March. In the minds of both parents the new little boy was to have been a girl to replace Tessie. Annetta had chosen a name for her—Louisa—her own mother's name. Tony did not hide his disgust when the boy arrived, but Annetta turned her love for the dead girl child into this bit of new life. She wished to call him Luigi, but Tony would have none of it. Nevertheless, at moments when Tony was roving his territory, she cuddled the little baby boy, would cross herself and gently whisper, "My Lulu". So when Tony had left the room after beating little Frank, she murmured tenderly to the whimpering, quivering child, "My Lulu".

It mattered little that Tony's clanging wagon ultimately developed into the Calux Scrap Metal Company, verbosely and expensively incorporated by lawyer Amerino; that Jerry, the surly older boy, went into his father's business after playing a bruising game at guard for the Flushing High School; that a sister, Maria, arrived when Frank was ten. She had come too late for Annetta to shift the object of her love, or for president Tony of the Metal Company to divert more than a casual thought to her from his precious heaps of battered scrap, now hoisted by huge cranes into steel hopper cars and motor trucks for direct shipment to the mills.

Nor did it matter that Frank followed Jerry into the business after three years of mediocrity at the Flushing School, nor that Frank's wife presented two grandchildren to aging Annetta and Tony. Tony never forgave Frank's failure to fulfill the role of a girl his parents had predestined for him; Annetta never ceased to solace him with "My Lulu" when things went wrong.

After ten minutes the doctor's reflections on Calucci's past were interrupted by the patient.

"It's a funny thing, Doctor," he said, resuming his story, "that the old skunk should steal from the business. You know how it was. Jerry and me bought him out three years ago when the pneumonia and that abscess in his lung knocked him. We paid him sixty thousand dollars for it—that ain't chicken-feed, Doc—every cent of what it was worth. And then he was so unhappy with nothing to do that we gave him a job in the office—paid him forty dollars a week so he wouldn't feel that he wasn't good for nothing any more."

"What kind of a man would you say your father is?" inquired the doctor.

"Pop is a flare-up. He blows his top. When a feller needles him, he can't take it but he's mean to me and Mom—always complainin' Mom didn't know how to handle money. And he never went to church, even when he was so sick a coupla years ago and everybody thought he was going to croak, he wouldn't have nothin' to do with the priests. Pop said all they wanted was dough. And Mom told me he was an altar boy! And now the old bastard is stealing from us—funny, isn't it? I can't figure it out. I know you usually don't answer such questions, Doctor, but what do you think about it?"

"It's not what I think about it but what you think that really counts, as I've told you often," answered Ford, using a phrase habitual with him when patients sought to put the responsibility for their decisions upon him. "But let's see. How long have the thefts been going on?" he asked, feeling his way cautiously.

"I can't tell. I have been able to trace it back for nine months—little amounts—about thirty dollars a week. Should I speak to him about it?"

"Why do you want to do that?" queried Ford hoping to bring out further reactions in the patient.

"It's all wrong—after what we've done for him. I ask you, does any man like being robbed—father or no father?" cried the patient sitting up on the couch and facing the doctor defiantly. "Besides, I've always been sore at him for the way he treated Mom."

"Why not ask your brother, Jerry, what he thinks? He is concerned, too, isn't he?" said the doctor.

"You know me and Jerry—we never agreed about anything since we was kids. He was always trying to bully me. And you know Jerry and cold cash—he's as tight and crooked as Pop. If he found it out he'd just come up from behind and knock the old thief's block off. How would you like to see Pop, Doc? Maybe he'd come over and you could kinda find out."

"No, I think not. You'd best handle it yourself. Perhaps you could let your father know indirectly that you are aware of what is going on—that is, if you wish merely to stop the money loss. Or, let the whole thing ride for a while," said Dr. Ford again avoiding the patient's attempt to involve him directly in the problem but seeking to defer any precipitate action on the part of the incensed son.

"That don't satisfy me. As usual, Doc, your clever passing the buck ain't worth a red cent to a fellow when something really important comes up,—a regular song and dance" growled the patient as he started to slouch out of the office.

One week later, as he lay on the couch, Calucci after a long silence remarked to the doctor:

"You remember when I told you the other day about Pop and his stealing. Well, something inside me just made me have to follow it up. I just couldn't lay off. Now, would you believe it, by tracing back on the books I see that the old crook began to gyp us about three months after we gave him that job—just out of the kindness of our hearts. Of course it was me who thought of giving the old man something to do just to get him out of the house and keep Mom from going crazy with all his grouching. To tell the truth I felt sort of sorry for him, too, wandering around town all alone and lonely. You bet Jerry didn't want to do it."

"So did you speak to your father about it?" asked the doctor.

"Yes, I did. I told it to him today. Just went up to him and spit it out right to his face—told him the accounts were short and he was a God damn robber."

"Don't you think you were pretty severe with him?" asked the doctor quietly. "And what did he say?"

"Nothing. He seemed to get white as a sheet, but he's awful pale now anyway. He just looked straight ahead—sorta blank —couldn't look me in the eye. Then he bowed his head, turned his back on me and just wobbled slowly out of the office. He stopped and looked back at me for a minute and it seemed to me like he was getting ready to cry. I guess I hit him kinda hard."

Two days later when Frank Calucci entered Dr. Ford's office the stoop in his shoulders, the forward bend in his neck, the dragging walk all seemed more pronounced than usual. His thick, crisp hair had suddenly become grayer above the temples. He lay motionless on the couch for a long while. Ford did not wish to break the ominous silence and waited for what might come. The room became so unnaturally still that one could almost hear the silence.

"Doc", Calucci said at last in an empty, toneless voice, "the old man's dead."

Doctor Ford's usual composure was shaken. With an inflection which unconsciously revealed his shock and surprise, he echoed:

"Dead?"

"Dead," continued Calucci in the same tone, flat and listless. "We found him the morning after I spoke to him, down in the shed of his old junk yard by the Long Island tracks—dead. He was dangling from a rope."

"Have you been much affected by it?" queried the doctor.

"Oh, me, I've never had any feelings anyway. I never wuz able to squeeze out a tear over nothing. I can drop a hundred in a crap game and don't even feel sorry. The only thing that makes me cry is when somebody is good to some kid in a movie—then I bawl my head off like a baby. I told you all that hooey before," said the patient. "And I told you I never could bring my own kids a toy or candy. Guess I'm a hard-hearted guy, Doc."

"Perhaps not so tough deep down as you like to pretend, as I've told you before," replied Dr. Ford kindly. "How about scenes of success, love, murder or violent death? Don't they affect you?"

"They don't give me no feelings at all."

Then Frank Calucci grew silent again. His face showed no expression, no regret, no pang of remorse. He relaxed as if very tired. Before long Doctor Ford could hear his heavy, regular breathing transformed into a light snore. Finally he settled into a deep sleep which dismantled his mind of the threatening thoughts of guilt which crept upon him from within and relieved him from obligations which death always brings to a family. Now he himself lay as if dead.

This was not the first time that Calucci had shown this unusual reaction of somnolence, but of late he had become decreasingly liable to these attacks and they had seemed less severe. The doctor had hoped that they were about to cease altogether, but the patient's sleep now was as complete as any the doctor had observed during the long course of treatment.

"This man," thought Dr. Ford discouraged, "is so constantly on the defensive even with me. He succeeds in shutting out impressions and influences which might bring about a change in his mode of thinking, although he came to me for help. Of course there are all sorts of resistances which patients contrive against giving up a neurosis and getting well—talking about and around the issues, not talking at all, constant fault-finding with the method or the doctor or both, excessive humility and agreeing in order to avoid discussion. But this fellow has the most complete armor I have ever met. What can I do if he continues to use deep sleep as a defensive weapon against my efforts to assist him?"

Doctor Ford rose from his chair and went to the window looking down on the foliage in Gramercy Park just beginning to turn yellow and bronze in the first frosts of October. The sounds from the stream of automobiles rounding the square in a steady procession contrasted with the sleeping patient behind him. Then the Doctor went to his flat-topped desk strewn with pamphlets, a memo pad and a tooled leather tray filled with notes on patients. He straightened them out carelessly and then began to read a typed manuscript on the role of psychiatry in a general hospital. It was the third typing but he started to make interlinear corrections in pencil here and there. All the while he kept an eye on the sleeping patient who sometimes snored loudly. The doctor knew from previous experience the futility of trying to arouse him immediately. Then, when some time had passed, he moved to the head of the couch.

"Calucci," he called loudly. "Calucci, wake up! Wake up, Calucci!"

The patient grunted, and very slowly and gradually roused himself.

"Ugh!" he said, looking around at Dr. Ford and yawning and rubbing his eyes. "I must have fallen asleep."

Then he stretched, composed his limbs, and in a calm, impersonal voice, took up his story as if no time had elapsed.

"Because of the funeral and lots of other things which'll come up, Doc, I don't believe I'll be able to see you again for a week or so. There'll be a lot to do. Mom needs me bad.

Of course she don't know anything of how this all happened. When I told her about it, she cried a little, but all she said was, 'My Lulu'."

A week later Frank Calucci's face wore as impenetrable a mask as ever as he came through the door from the waiting room into Ford's office. His head seemed a bit raised, his eyes moved less frequently from side to side.

"You know, it's funny, Doc," he began. "The old man made a will before he died, made it over a year ago. Pop sure had a plenty, more than any of us thought. It's funny, he left the house and ten thousand dollars to Mom, and not a cent to Jerry or Maria, although she certainly needs it with that dopey husband she married. It's funny. I guess the old man must have felt long ago it wasn't right what he was doing. Maybe he knew it was me made the job for him. Maybe the guilt goes further back than that, like you would say, Doc. Anyway, it's funny. The will reads: 'And all the remainder of my estate I give and bequeath to my beloved son, Frank Calucci.' "

"I guess I'm a funny gink, too," announced Frank Calucci about two weeks later as he flopped himself on the couch. "You see, Doc, we all met at big lawyer Amerino's office yesterday to discuss the will. Some stuffed shirt he is, but some classy office he's got. Pop paid for it all right. Pop never had no use for priests. Amerino was his god and god took a plenty from Pop for taking care of him. Anyway, God never let Pop get into jail. Did I tell you, Doc, Amerino and me are executors of the will. Jerry and Maria and Joe, her dumb cluck of a husband, all sat around and when we had been there talking a lot of nothing for a while, then Amerino says, 'Well, Frank, as you know, the residual estate is all yours'."

"It's funny", Frank continued, "something funny happened to me that minute, Doc. I felt like crying but I just said, 'Share and share alike—three parts'. The others didn't say one word but you could see that goofy Joe's greedy eyes pop."

"Quite an unusually generous thing for you to do, wasn't it," said Ford impassively.

"But that isn't all", continued Calucci ignoring the doctor's comment. "Pop had a little black iron safe he must'a got for junk forty years back. Nobody but him knew the combination and we had to jimmy the lock. Well, back of old, yellow insurance papers, his naturalization certificate and such stuff, we found a cigar box filled with old jewelry. Where he got it even God or Amerino don't know. Anyway, Amerino had it there and said it was all mine. Some of it was just junk but not much. The old man must have picked it up in pawnshops, auctions and antique stores. I guess some of it might have been stolen goods he bought from crooks and second-story men in the early days. An old gold ring with a ruby big as your middle fingernail, maybe twenty old garnet brooches. He must have had a mania for them. Also a nugget of gold big as a walnut still attached to the rock it was found in, and then a scarf pin with a diamond big as your little fingernail—it must be worth a heap in these days when everything's booming."

"And what did you do with it?" inquired Ford.

"I saw Maria eyeing that big diamond. Then something funny came over me—I don't know what. 'It's yours,' I says to her. Funny, isn't it, Doc? Now I ask you, why did I do that. But don't tell me there was a sense of guilt back of it or any of that tripe you sometimes pull."

"I may be wrong, Calucci, but it may have been the glitter from the diamond that reawakened old feelings of guilt. Perhaps it was a little reminiscent of the glint from the shining pan you took when you were a child. You must remember it. Do you think that the memory of that day when your father thrashed you may have had something to do with your recent generosity after all? Of course, I mean ever so remotely," ventured Dr. Ford with a quiet smile.

"That old guilt stuff again. But it just don't get me a bit," replied Calucci rebelliously.

The patient reverted to immobility. He closed his eyes, the breathing became deep and he fell into a sound sleep. This quick symptom of retreat from life again discouraged and disappointed Dr. Ford who had hoped that the transient manifestation of generosity and feeling would continue. Was it possible, he asked himself, that in spite of his long efforts to release the patient from a life which had been devoid of feeling, the whole recent dramatic episode had already ceased to exist as a living experience? Would the image of old Tony dangling in the shed rise to haunt Frank waking? Would it be likely to crash the censorship of sleep in his dreams? Would the tragedy be enveloped and lost to immediate memory like a stone dropped in a quagmire and the patient continue for the rest of his life deprived of any feelings of love and joy—living from second to second, not from day to day, isolated and apart from reality—a zombie in the world of the living. . . .

No, Ford said to himself, this must not happen. It would require more patience and effort. In recent months flickers of emotion were proof that all was not dead in the patient. If doctor and patient continued their work, the chances were good that the battle might be won. Perhaps old Tony's violent death might hasten recovery. And now the patient responded immediately and alertly when Ford leaned over from his chair behind the couch and called very softly to the sleeping man, "Calucci, wake up".

VI

BUSY DOCTOR

Summer had come and with it a few humid days late in June when the steamy vapors rose from the baked asphalt of the city's streets. Before long Doctor Ford would be on his way to Europe, a custom which he now found some reason for renewing almost every year—either an international congress in Czecho-Slovakia, or Holland, or remote Russia, or if there were none the trip itself had become reason enough.

He left again on the Patria which made her slow pitching way over the Atlantic to the Azores and Lisbon and to the North African coastal towns and finally Italy. She had been his choice several times—a comfortable ship with spacious decks and salons so simple that one did not hesitate to lounge informally in them. Among his fellow-travelers he had always found a few whose ideas and manners were so like his own that it required little effort to become friendly with them.

On the third day out as he stood leaning back lazily against the rail in the warming sun and cooling breezes of the South Atlantic with a copy of *The Flowering of New England* in his hand, a tall, thin man of about forty-five, his own age, sauntered up and suggested affably, "How about a game of shuffleboard"? The stranger turned out to be a skilled and considerate opponent and also a doctor, drawn to Ford by those intangibles which so often attract doctors, ministers, socialites and gamblers to one another soon after members of the heterogeneous group on their floating hotel find themselves separated from their customary companions and haunts.

Doctor Charles Johnson was the name of Doctor Ford's new acquaintance. He lived in Pittsford, Connecticut, a surgeon and highly successful. He was a reserved, taciturn fellow whose brown, alert eyes showed not only initiative but determination. He mingled little with the passengers but seemed pleased with Ford's company.

One night as the ship was nearing the European mainland they were standing at the rail looking out over the ocean to where it seemed to merge with the clear, starlit sky. There had been long pauses in their desultory talk that night—mostly trivialities about medical cases and personalities. After a particularly long lapse Doctor Johnson quietly remarked:

"You know, Doctor Ford, I feel both very lonely and lonesome on this trip. I had thought until the last moment that a good friend of mine, Bob Whitmore, the dean of the Episcopal Church of my town might come along, but at the last moment he couldn't get away."

"Well," replied Ford, "why don't you take your wife along when you go abroad on a trip like this."

Doctor Johnson turned slowly to face Ford and the light in his eyes became visible in the darkness.

"Would you believe it," he said, "my wife and I have not been away together on a single vacation since we married."

"How does Mrs. Johnson take that. No protests?" asked Ford.

"In a mild way," said Johnson. "But she is self-effacing and urges me to take a vacation." Then apparently released by an uncustomary outburst of confidence he continued with greater animation and more freely than was his wont. "She says there'll still be plenty of work to do when I'm dead and maybe still a few doctors alive to do it. But you know how it is with a busy doctor—his work is always unfinished. Always another new patient to be seen or another look at the fellow you operated on a week ago. We had half planned a little trip for our tenth wedding anniversary but for some reason it didn't come off. I remember now—a ruptured gastric ulcer." Then his voice became subdued and wistful as he said:

"Do you know what it feels like to be more lonely and alone when you're with your wife than when you are all by yourself?"

Doctor Ford did not reply but he recognized the feeling— the feeling of isolation of which certain patients often complained—the loneliness which is so intense and painful to the young fellow who paces the porch while within gay couples glide to lively tunes. It is even more devastating to the girl who spends a long, long time powdering her nose in the ladies' room because she cannot feel at ease with her chatty friends playing at bridge at an afternoon tea. Such a sense of isolation is overwhelming as compared with that felt by the lonely man sauntering down a city avenue or following a woodland path. The incongruity of his own glumness and gaiety of others does not force itself upon him. The solitary wanderer in tune with his surroundings may further be solaced and comforted by the absence of disturbing contrasts and impacts calling attention to his human deficiencies.

Johnson made no comment and Ford stayed silent waiting for a continuation of the story. He felt sure that additional revelations would follow now that Johnson's protective shell which enveloped long repressed feeling had been weakened through solitude and the darkness of night. Added to these forces, silence on the part of the listener is one of the most encouraging for confidences. Finally the expected came.

"I'm sure, Doctor Ford, my true confession which I have just thrust so abruptly upon you means to you as a psychiatrist that there must be more behind it. Of course there is. I need not tell you that my marriage has been as much of a failure as my professional work has been a success and satisfaction. Perhaps I should never have married. Sometimes I think that it might have been better for my wife, at least, if we never had. But to get back to my problem, if it does not bore you." He paused expectantly and again received the encouragement of Ford's silence.

"It's a fairly common story as you must well know—among doctors anyway. You see, my father was a Unitarian minister in a small town in Connecticut not far from Pittsford where I am located. If any man was a Puritan he was—a Puritan in spite of the theological liberalism of his church. He might as well have been an old New England Calvinist. He wished me to follow in his footsteps. He disliked frivolity of all kinds and I, being naturally of a studious bent, wanted to study a profession but definitely not the ministry. Medicine was my first choice and a conscientious medical student and faithful intern I became."

"What kind of a woman is Mrs. Johnson?" ventured Ford.

"Simple and the kind of a girl they call nice in a small town—little distinction from half a dozen other nice girls. We paired off together at church and high school socials. Eventually she began to teach school right in town. By the time I had finished my internship we were both twenty-six— she already in the old-maid class. A woman of twenty-six is old in a town where the high school seniors set the social pace."

"And why did you marry her?" asked Ford simply.

"Candidly that's difficult to say. Sometimes I think that the ease of it all decided me—no courting—no trouble. Maybe I didn't know how to unload the whole situation—maybe I wanted to spare myself the inconvenience and embarrassment of breaking off. I knew I would merely have to ask her. My father married us and would you believe it, the only thought which passed through my mind as I mechanically repeated the words of the ceremony was, 'I hope that some day I will love this woman'." He paused for several minutes and stared into the darkness. "She is a semi-invalid."

"What do you mean?" asked Ford.

"She had tuberculosis in childhood and a t.b. knee. It is all healed now but she is still delicate and has a slight limp. You know, sometimes I think I married her only because she was sick—maybe I wanted a patient for a wife—wanted to practice medicine all the time right in my own home."

"I do not wish to appear inquisitive, Doctor Johnson, but did your love for her ever develop?"

"My contact with my wife has remained perfunctory and tactile," responded Johnson dryly.

Both men became quiet and finally Johnson said abruptly, "It was good to talk with you, Doctor Ford. In Pittsford there is no one to whom I can really talk excepting Bob Whitmore of whom I spoke earlier. He is some one I can respect. We have had many chats for hours about philosophy, religion, and life in general. Often I would drop in at his study in the rectory next to the church for a high ball after a night operation at the hospital when I was fagged out. It is a large, homelike room—a haven to me. But sometimes one can talk about purely personal affairs better to a stranger."

"Yes, I've noticed how often people tell the most intimate affairs to persons whom they meet traveling in the coupés of European trains," agreed Ford. "Usually they reach the climax of their story just before they are about to arrive at the station where they are getting out."

"Well, I guess I've detained you long enough," said Johnson abruptly. "I'll turn in. Good-night and thank you, Doctor Ford."

"Won't you have a nightcap before you go?"

"No, not to-night, thanks," and he walked off slowly.

An hour later when Ford stepped out of the smoking room he caught a glimpse of Johnson's tall figure still pacing slowly around the deck. Ford thought it best to leave him alone with his meditations.

Doctor Ford answered the telephone which rang just as he was about to leave for lunch at noon and the operator said, "Long distance, Pittsford, Connecticut, calling Doctor Ben Ford," and after a minute or two an unfamiliar voice said, "Is this Doctor Ford? Well, this is Doctor Johnson, Charles Johnson."

"Not Doctor Johnson who used to beat me at shuffleboard on the Patria five years ago?"

"Yes, the old champion himself."

"Well, how are you—glad to hear from you."

"Oh, I'm fine, fine. Do you happen to remember we had a long talk one night looking out over the ocean."

"Oh, yes. I do remember it."

"Well, I have a patient who puzzles me—I guess he's a patient—for you. I'd like you to see him right away—to-night if you can."

"That will be almost impossible."

"Don't you think that you might manage to," pleaded Johnson. "You see—if I must say it—the patient is me. I certainly would appreciate it beyond words if you could give me a little of your time at once. I can be down soon. It's only about three hours by fast train—any time to-night you say is all right with me."

The urgency in Doctor Johnson's voice betrayed an unusual anxiety which Ford had not associated with his composed steamer companion.

"All right—I'll surely see you—we'll make it at eight," said Ford after looking at his calendar and noting that the perennial paper on "Newer Methods in Psychotherapy" by an ambitious younger colleague which he had agreed to discuss that evening had the last place on the program. He would be able to make it even if Doctor Johnson proved to be circumstantial, which was not likely to be the case.

Promptly at eight o'clock the door bell rang and Doctor

Ford answered it himself. The man who had entered looked taller than Ford recollected him—well near six feet—possibly because his expression was drawn and he had grown thinner. Dr. Johnson forced an apologetic smile as he greeted Ford and they walked into the office together. He refused the chair which Ford offered and began the conversation at once to relieve his embarrassment and tension.

"You know it's a darn shame for me to come down here to dump my rotten eggs into your basket. But I have had you in my mind ever since that night on the Patria—the eggs were just beginning to get stale then. Now they're rotten and one of them has just cracked and the stench of it nauseates me. It's a nurse at our hospital—and I need your professional advice, if you'll be kind enough, Doctor Ford."

"Why of course, Johnson, if I can."

"But I want this to be professional, on a strictly professional basis—fee in advance if you wish," he said flashing a smile.

"Oh, we'll see about that later", answered Ford as he sank into the worn leather swivel chair behind the dented flat-topped desk.

Johnson lit a cigarette and began to walk nervously up and down the room. His tired brown eyes began to fire and finally he exploded with a vehemence which seemed incongruous with his generally restrained manner, "Jesus, I must have been crazy about that woman—maybe I still am. That's what I've come to see you about."

"How long has it been going on?"

"Oh, for over three years, I should say. Remember my remark on the trip about loneliness? Pathetic, wasn't it, but in my case true. I guess my loneliness has much to do with my predicament."

"And what kind of a woman is this nurse—this woman with whom you evidently do not feel alone?"

"She is difficult to describe and there's something of a mystery about her. You see she's not an American, she's German—North German near the Danish border and she has the features of the blonde type which is common there. To me she's a very attractive woman with a most perfect set of teeth," said Johnson warming to his subject, "and she's tall—as tall as I, almost—square shoulders, a full, deep chest and long legs which are not too full at the hips—that is, not quite proportionate to her chest and torso."

"Yes, and I assume quite different from your demure wife. But surely she has some qualities besides a fair complexion and a full chest," said Ford with a slight smile. "What's her name, by the way? Only her first name, just as a matter of identification."

Doctor Johnson's face flushed as if he had been rebuked. "Johanna—I call her Yonnie. You remember I am a surgeon and she is the operating room nurse—a mighty clever one, too. She's never out of sorts, at times even buoyant and can enjoy life. She knows how to have fun and almost succeeded in teaching me. She is tireless, efficient, with the endurance and nerve of a man. I've got a pretty good assistant just now and between him and her, they're the best team I've ever worked with. Practice is getting heavier all the time and without her I'd have to train in some new girl. Even though you're far removed from the scalpel and clamp, Doctor Ford, you must know how hard it is to find any one really competent and also understanding."

"Yes, I know the advantage of teamwork—of having a secretary who is sympathetic to your aims and takes interest in what you're attempting to do—a resounding board—if you will. Yonnie, if I may call her that, does seem to fit in nicely with your needs in more ways than one. That's one of the troubles with too many of us fellows. Our job swallows us so that after twenty years many of us never seem to show any real enthusiasm unless we are talking to each other about our own interesting case or medical politics and hospital gossip."

"There is safety as well as virtue in keeping busy," said Johnson in a voice so sanctimonious that it might have been his father preaching from the pulpit.

"Nothing truer," agreed Ford, "and when a helpful and attractive woman can be unobtrusively drawn into this absorbing picture, she is likely to give an additional zest to the work so that after a while it begins to glow in her image— and the other way round as well."

"Yes, and Yonnie is rare," agreed Johnson with mounting warmth. "She came to us from Massachusetts General Hospital with a most flattering recommendation from Thomas Aylsworth, the fellow who's a whiz on stomach resection. She had experience in Copenhagen. Her father was a general in the German Army. I have seen his picture—there's a good deal of resemblance between Yonnie and her father—even in his uniform and helmet, epaulets and all—something stately, almost aristocratic in them both."

"A Brunhilda, it seems," smiled Ford as he noted Johnson returning to his nurse's physical characteristics.

"Perhaps," replied Johnson. "Anyway, the affinity to the woman certainly has grown upon me. It's gotten to be terrible. Some men might not find her attractive but sometimes when our forearms touch over the wound during an operation, or her thigh brushes up against mine as we stand at the operating table, I am thrown out of my stride for just a moment. It's happened more and more often during the last three or four months. I don't know if intentionally— sometimes I know it is on my part, at least. Maybe I ought to marry her."

"Does your wife suspect?"

"The thought is as far from her mind as not voting for Hoover for a second time. She's a Bates and since the Civil

War it has been next thing to heresy for a Bates to vote anything but Republican. Of course, I think that some of the people about the hospital have their suspicions about Yonnie and me, even though I like to think that they have not."

Ford began to jot down a few notes in pencil on a small pad. He might have them transcribed later or more likely, file them away as they were, illegible to anyone but himself. Doctor Johnson eyed the action distrustingly, apparently remembered that he was there as a patient, and made no protest.

"These hospital scandals have always annoyed me," he continued, "and we've had one or two nasty ones right in our own little hospital in Pittsford which reached the newspapers. I'd hate to be the 'him' of one of them, with every member of the staff wishing you an over-polite 'good-morning' as he passes you in corridors and then making a bee-line for the staff room to hear the latest rumor from our associate obstetrician who is as gossipy and vicious-tongued as the proverbial village old-maid."

"I come in contact with it often enough at the City Memorial," agreed Ford, "where they call me in occasionally for an hysterical aphonia or to pass on some noisy patient they wish to transfer to a psychopathic hospital. It's sometimes hard to escape a corridor consultation with some member of the staff who is having real trouble with his wife or is worried about a 'good friend of his', euphemistically himself, or about his 'problem' child who isn't doing as well as he should at school."

"That's all very well," interrupted Johnson, "but I never thought anything like this could happen to me—at fifty. Yonnie has been changing all my habits. I'm taking more time off from work and have become interested in hunting and skiing, of all things, at my age."

"I suppose Yonnie is fond of shooting."

"How did you guess that? Yes, she's a skilled horsewoman as well as marvellous at skeet shooting. She has an old German Army Mauser rifle—one once used by her father and she handles it like an expert. She says she once shot a buck up in Vermont after he had started to bound away."

"Why were you so impressed when you saw Yonnie shoot the buck?"

"How did you suspect I was there?"

"Since you ask me: the admiration and enthusiasm in your voice—in which an element of horror and astonishment were also mingled."

"Well, it's so," nodded Johnson, not greatly disturbed by Ford's observation. He paused for a minute or so, with his eyes fixed in space as if revisualizing the scene. Then he continued to relate his story impersonally.

"I suppose it will be unnecessary for me to confirm what you have already gathered. Yonnie and I have been together in New Hampshire and other places a number of times. I have not been away on a long vacation since that trip to Europe when I was fortunate enough to meet you—five years ago, wasn't it? Now I take my time off in the autumn. I find it conditions me better for the hard work of the winter. It seemed entirely proper that my operating room nurse, who is such a valuable, shall I say, indispensable unit of our team, should have her holiday at the same time. We spent days, even a week or so, of happiness together. Would you believe it, Doctor Ford, for the first time in my life I have ever loved a woman—wholly and fully. It gave me an inkling of what a truly satisfying relationship can mean."

"Then you have been the gainer in this affair, at least in one great particular," remarked Ford.

If this comment registered, Johnson gave no indication of it. The reticent man's tongue had been loosed. Now he released his account fluently, almost eagerly.

"The need to love grew—it absorbed and overwhelmed me.

During the past year I developed an urge to brush up on surgical technique—found it necessary to visit some prominent clinics in Boston, Nasmyth's in New York, thoracic surgeon, you may know him. And we even went to Johns Hopkins in Baltimore. There were times off for Yonnie as well—she always looked forward to these trips. The whole thing seemed so thoroughly natural and feasible but we had to be discreet. Just lately she is showing less desire for the trips and also for me."

"Perhaps she is a woman always in search of new achievements—may I say conquests—and excitements. The kind who loses interest in the man as soon as she feels she has won his full attention. Then she must seek another to reassure her of her charms," observed Ford. "In its larger aspects yours is not a new story. I have heard it with variations half a dozen times from women as well as men and in all classes of society."

Johnson again gave no indication that he had heard and rambled on.

"My love, call it a mad infatuation if you will, began to engross me and monopolize my thoughts day and night. With Mrs. Johnson, poor thing, I became more demanding and impatient about the most trivial things. To try to escape from myself I take long rides alone in my car in the hilly country west of Pittsford. Sometimes I get out of the car and go afoot—trying to walk my troubles out of my system. It's soothing to frayed nerves to take a tramp amidst the autumn foliage. Sometimes I think I am going completely to pieces. For several weeks I have been taking sedatives at night."

"Only at night?" asked Ford.

"Yes and during the day as well—luminal—far too much of it. I have become carping and critical of Yonnie at operations—ready to snap her head off if she makes the slightest mistake, and even worse if she makes a suggestion."

"Any particular thing which annoyed you?" interrupted Ford with a specific question such as he seldom asked directly of patients.

Johnson reflected before he replied. "Yes, Yonnie smokes cigarettes a great deal. I suppose she's had the bad habit for a long time but I never noticed it much until recently. She would lie back in a chair after an operation, inhale and blow the smoke out in two streams through her nostrils. It disgusted me so that at times I could barely restrain myself from slapping her face. It seemed so contradictory to my ideas of her. She is not a fastidious woman but extremely cleanly."

"Perhaps you regarded the stream of smoke as defiance," said Ford dryly.

Now, too, Johnson ignored the comment and hurried on. "I found myself having more and more spare time. As I told you before, a new resident, a young Southerner, just a kid, came to our hospital last July. Not long ago Yonnie and he began going horseback riding together. It happened several times. I have always been a little impotent at horseback riding even as a young man and have gotten worse in recent years. I suspected that they were making up to each other. Life seemed to stretch out before me like a dreary, brown, Western desert, having no landmarks."

"To whom have you told this story before?" asked Ford, ignoring Johnson's lamentation and choice of the word "impotent", although he made a mental note and evaluated both.

"Why, no one. What makes you think so?"

"You said to me that you had already told me of the new resident—it must have been to some one else you spoke." Then Ford said sharply and almost brusquely, "Let's have it."

Perhaps the greatest skill of the psychiatrist lies in the timing of his comments and interpretations. The when and how is often as important as what he says. The decision to reveal a certain thing at a certain time does not always come as the result of deliberate consideration. Experience which has crystallized as something called intuition may determine this timing almost unconsciously.

"Very adroit aren't you, Doctor Ford," snapped Johnson, with a display of anger and sarcasm in his voice which verged on a sneer. He had just lit his third cigarette. Now he put it out by crushing the burning tip against an ash tray with such force that the cigarette bent.

The change in Johnson's manner convinced Ford that his inference had been right but he did not press the point. Previous experience had taught him that when a situation such as Doctor Johnson's had dragged out over a period of years it was some alarming incident in the immediate present that drove the patient to seek help from the physician—that some crisis had developed which had increased the person's tension to the breaking point. The time at which a patient came for consultation was often quite as significant as the problem he brought. Ford puffed slowly at a half-smoked cigar. He had to wait only a few minutes before Johnson regained his composure and continued.

"What a jackass I am. You must pardon my outburst of irritability—I'm not quite myself. How you startled, almost shocked me. Of course you're right—it is just because I have told my story to some one else that I have come to you for help. You may remember my friend of the cloth, Whitmore, whom I mentioned once or twice on the Patria."

"Of course," replied Ford, "that old friend of yours and a rarity in New England, a progressively minded minister in a cathedral church."

"Well, I spoke with him last night. The anxiety and doubting about Yonnie—call it crazed jealousy, if you will, and have it over with—had driven me to a frenzy. I had tried for a few days to be cool, detached and impersonal—all in vain. Then I began to pity myself. It's a sterile and selfish emotion."

"Generally, yes," agreed Ford, "it leaves no room for anything stimulating and strangles the desire for action. Of course, sometimes self-estimation if properly gauged can lead to change but self-commiseration seldom does."

"Wallowing in self-pity led me nowhere, produced nothing, only more self-pity. In desperation I called up my clerical friend from my office at about ten o'clock yesterday evening and asked him if I could come down to the rectory to talk things over with him. He responded most cordially. Then I called Mrs. Johnson and told her that I had a serious case I must see. She was sympathetic with me, reminded me to be sure to wear my heavier fall coat and woolen gloves—the nights are already quite nippy up in our hills. Then I jumped into my coupe and drove around the sparsely settled country just outside our town for a while."

"And why that?"

"A superfluous question, Doctor Ford. I presume you have divined that also. But I'll omit my resentment this time. I did not want to appear to be too eager about my visit to the Dean. But, yes, two thoughts really obsessed my mind—one was to speed up the car and crash into a row of old maples which line the State road at a point where a long, straight stretch takes a sudden turn—the other was to roll off the road down an embankment about three miles outside of town on the way coming in. It seemed in my insanity the only thing left for me to do. As you see I could bring myself to do neither. I have been called to fatal accidents at both these places but two or three of the people remained permanent cripples. Finally after about half an hour of aimless and frantic riding about I pulled up in front of the rectory next to Whitmore's church. By the time Whitmore himself had answered my ring a minute or two later, I had regained, externally at least, my self-possession. He greeted me heartily and we walked into his study."

"What type of man is the minister?" asked Ford, "the man to whom you first brought your troubles. As I look back now upon the references you made to your friend, I am reminded that you mentioned little concerning his personality though once or twice you quoted his views on social questions. If I remember rightly he had been a strong supporter of the League of Nations and an admirer of President Wilson—something of a worldly individual, modern and liberal, in theory at least if not so ardent in practice."

"What a memory you have, Doctor Ford! That's correct. Maybe I should give you a few details about him. First, he has been a widower for some ten years. He's about my own age, nearly six feet tall, slim and slightly round-shouldered. He has the pallor of a sedentary man, eyes deep set, nose slightly aquiline. Oh, yes, he's politic and circumspect and perhaps shy. Maybe in that respect he resembles me. We may have other traits in common now that I come to think of it. The ladies are particularly fascinated by him and many of the old maids and widows in town have set their caps for him—unsuccessfully."

"Does the minister live alone?" asked Ford.

"Yes, just now. He has a fourteen year old boy—an only child—away at one of our good Connecticut 'prep' schools. So most of the time he's a bachelor and spends most of his days looking after the needs of his parishioners. He's a busy man with all he undertakes for the town's social welfare."

"His life and interests seem not dissimilar to your own."

Ford's impassivity annoyed Johnson and he resumed his story without replying.

"The study is a large, cheerful room which opens directly to the street and the living quarters are back of it. A brisk fire was burning in the grate, his Morris chair beside it, when Whitmore in a somewhat worn, brown dressing gown welcomed me in. On a reading table, face down, lay a copy of Walter Lippman's *Preface to Morals*. 'Have a glass of sherry or a high ball, Charlie', he said, drawing up another easy chair for me. He went to a wall closet built in among the bookshelves, produced a bottle of Dry Sack and poured us each a generous glass.

" 'Winter isn't far away. I'm dabbling over my Thanksgiving sermon—bringing an old theme up to date—vide Walter Lippman. He's a keen commentator on our post-war problems'.

" 'Much as I would like to chin with you about the Depression and all that,' I said to him, 'you must know that I would not be down here at this time of night just when I'm rushed to death in practice if there were not something imperative on my mind. I've been under a terrific strain lately.'

"Whitmore lolled back in his chair and became attentive. He did nothing to draw me out. Like you, Doctor Ford, the minister has learned the value of listening. Then I told him my story much as I have to you. Of course he knew the setting—my father's clerical calling, my general lack of interest in my wife and home, my slavery to my profession. I expatiated on my overwork and my unreasonable critical attitude toward my wife, stalled a bit, deferred as long as I could any mention of Yonnie. Then I exploded that I was in love with her. I implied my infidelity to my wife, finally came out into the open and burst forth that lately a torturing jealousy had been violently aroused by that Southern youngster and his horseback rides with Yonnie and how it was all consuming me.

"Then Whitmore looked at me steadily and said with an odd constraint in his voice which I understand better now, 'Charlie, you ought to take yourself in hand. Those are bad ideas—very disturbing ideas. Don't let them get the upper hand of you'.

" 'I know, I know', I cried out. 'That's why I came to you. I feel trapped in a squirrel cage and find no way out. I've helped many a lame dog over a stile. Help me now. What would you do?'

"Whitmore said nothing," continued Johnson. "He had slumped in his chair, his elbow resting on the arm of the chair and his hand supporting his head but he did not appear to be thinking of my problem. The fire had died down and it was becoming chilly in the room. Suddenly the telephone rang. The sharp noise seemed to crash the stillness and startled us both. The phone stood on a desk right next to where I was sitting so that Whitmore had to pass back of my chair to answer it. He removed the receiver from the hook and in that second which it took for him to get balanced on the side of the desk before he put the receiver to his ear I heard, 'Hal-low there'.

"The voice was Yonnie's. I had heard those very words— that German intonation—time and time again when I had picked up the receiver in my own office late at night. Whitmore became pale and excited. After listening a moment he almost shouted, 'No, I say. You cannot come here now'. He did not look at me—he did not have to affirm my suspicion. For a minute or more he kept the receiver to his ear. Then he said softly, 'Not to-night'.

"Neither of us spoke. He sank back into his chair looking blanched. My mind began churning so violently that it seemed to me Whitmore must hear its vibrations. I put on my coat and found refuge in my coupe. I wanted to be alone in the whole world and in the dark."

A brief spasmodic movement shook the body of Doctor Johnson. He drew a handkerchief from his pocket, held it to his eyes for a moment and when he removed it his lean cheeks glistened with a thin stain of tears.

"I hope, Doctor Ford," he said, "that you will pardon this display of weakness."

"I don't think it an evidence of weakness to give way to emotion, Johnson," said Ford simply and kindly.

"Well," replied Johnson, "in the small New England town where I was raised it would be so considered."

In a minute or so he asked quite calmly, "And now do you think I have been, I am, completely crazy?"

"Not in the least. Most of us have lived through some such disappointment in our teens. Perhaps, as I have said before, the faithless Yonnie is that kind of fickle woman always in search of new conquests, new victims. It reassures her of her own desirability to men, young and old. But sometimes the victims also profit from a costly experience—maybe you will be well rid of her."

Doctor Johnson rose from a chair, began to walk slowly up and down the room, then sank back into another chair and let his head fall into his hands. He stared ahead and then he said, "Perhaps I needed a jolt like this."

"Sometimes it takes a shock to bring a man to his senses—and it need not be the jolt of a collision of a new automobile with a telegraph pole either," said Ford lightly.

"Yes," Johnson assented gravely, "I feel a sense of relief—better in a numb way. I am not impatient with the affair but weary from it. I feel as though I had gotten rid of something and had clarified something very real though indefinable. Vaguely I sense there are other solutions, other ways. The filthy situation seems less distasteful even though I'm not entirely certain of the future. The experience has left me very limp. Mrs. Johnson and her unswerving loyalty and devoted attention come to my mind."

"And maybe also her love which you could not reciprocate," said Ford simply, and he glanced at the flat clock on his desk.

"I still have time to run up to that Psychiatric Society meeting where I promised to discuss a paper on a time worn topic—'New Ways in Psychotherapy'—by Sidney Silverman, a younger man but promising. Maybe you'll come with me. The paper won't be too long and Silverman presents his stuff well. It will be old wine poured out of new bottles with a grand new label or two. But that's just as well if the wine is good. And later maybe we can have a leisurely talk and friendly bite together. They may also be soothing to shattered nerves—as calming sometimes as the rustle of autumn leaves underfoot and the blotches of red and russet in your beautiful Connecticut country-side."

Johnson rose to accompany him. He looked at Ford with a steady, kindly gaze and held out his hand. Then he said, "I will not thank you, Doctor Ford, but may I tell you my appreciation of your attention." Johnson's face lighted up pleasantly, as he added, "not to mention your skill. I'm thinking of the jolt you gave me a while ago with that inescapable 'Let's have it'!"

VII

THE VISITOR

Miss Rosalie Stein stepped lightly—for she wished to prevent the creaking of the old boards—down the dark stairway leading from the second floor to the front hall. Then she turned back past the unused front parlor and the dismal, dark-paneled dining room. Pausing at the head of the rear stairs, which descended to the basement kitchen, she called in her refined voice, for the moment almost musical, to the cook below.

"Sophie, if Doctor Mayer comes to see Papa, tell him I couldn't wait. And if my sister, Hilda, should come, tell her the same. And if Doctor Max should come, tell him too. I've got to go to the doctor's again."

"Dot's all right, Miss Rosalie, don't vorry. Everything vill be all right. I'll go up to see if Papa vants someting in a little vile," Sophie called back reassuringly without stopping her ironing. Then with an extra pressure on her iron, she muttered, "Don't vorry, Hilda and Doctor Max von't come. Dey never comes to see der fater."

"And be sure the blinds are dark in Papa's room. And if Doctor Mayer does come, you go up with him and remember to tell him Papa isn't eating," called Rosalie as she turned toward the heavy mahogany front door. She swung it open briskly, passed quickly through the shallow vestibule smelling of furniture polish and almost skipped down the flight of brownstone steps into the crisp air of a late September morning. Then she started with the mincing gait of the spinster rapidly westward towards the subway station on Broadway.

Not even a fleeting thought crossed her mind of the inconvenience or discomfort of the long subway ride to the doctor's office on Gramercy Park with its change and underground walk among the jostling throngs in the shuttle.

This was the day for which she had been impatiently, eagerly waiting: her first appointment with Dr. Ford after his return from his vacation trip abroad. This time he had said something vague about visiting Sweden and Russia. Her pulse quickened as she went, a flush began to creep into her pale, wrinkling face, her deep gray-blue eyes began to shine. For over two years now these visits three or four times each week to Doctor Ford had been the only relief in the monotony of her life.

As she stepped into the elevator to go up to the doctor's office the garrulous, old elevator man greeted her with a welcoming smile. "Charming day, Miss. Quite a stranger. I know —the sixteenth floor." Her heart began beating rapidly again as it had so often on previous visits and the elevator moved upward far too slowly. As she walked into the waiting room, its reassuring familiarity gave her the feeling of safety and shelter. She lit a cigarette,—smoking had been acquired since she began treatment—and as she flicked ashes she noted with satisfaction the deep red rouge stain in the mouth end. Rouge, as well as smoking, had been practices which her father had forbidden her.

When Dr. Ford, bronzed and almost ruddy from the wind and sun of the return ocean voyage, opened the door to admit her, an exuberant smile brightened her exceedingly plain face and gave to it momentarily something of a spiritual beauty. She flashed an appreciative, almost amorous look at the physician as she remarked in her well-bred manner:

"I am so very glad you're back, Doctor. I do hope that your vacation was all that you'd hoped for."

She let her eyes rove happily around the large room with its walls on one side lined with high built-in bookshelves, its

open fireplace on the other, its water colors of peaceful land-
and seascapes, oddities in bronze and glass gathered from distant places. Then, like a well-trained child who had made a
polite curtsy to company, she crossed to her customary place
on the leather couch without expecting a reply from the
doctor. He in turn took his seat behind her. The ceremony
performed it seemed to them both as if no time had passed
since they last discussed her troubles.

She had dressed with unusual care for the occasion, and had
visited the hairdresser for the first permanent to which she
had ever treated herself. Her fading yellow hair had acquired
a slight sheen. Her new dress was almost identical with the
one she had last worn—a blue silk, collar and cuffs of immaculate white embroidery, sheer silk stockings, and alligator
pumps. Most of her dresses were but variations of this style—
the costume had become almost a uniform. Today she had
added a slim strand of yellow-tinged pearls, an inheritance
from her mother. They lay limply on her neck, lax with the
folds of middle-age. From her came the faint odor of a
delicate perfume.

After waiting in vain for a few minutes for the patient to
speak, Doctor Ford said cordially in a delayed response to
his patient's entrance question.

"Thank you, Miss Stein. Things went well enough with me
this summer and I hope with you. I think I told you my
trip was to be to Scandinavia and to Russia. Yes, the visit to
Russia was enlightening and yet disappointing from a medical standpoint. At least I learned definitely one thing: that
their social system has not eliminated mental troubles as some
of our enthusiastic American medical travelers would have
had us believe. You can't legislate people out of their heritage of infantile memories or prevent emotional conflicts by
law. And how has the world been treating you?"

It was a perfunctory question. As the physician cast a
scrutinizing glance from his vantage point behind the recum-

bent patient he had noted that the momentary radiance had vanished from Miss Stein's yellowish-white countenance, that the accordion furrows between her eyes had become deeply fixed. The tenseness which pervaded her entire being showed itself in quick muscular twitchings visible in her thin, bare forearm, and even in the muscles of the legs through her sheer stockings.

"Oh, it's such a relief to know you are back, Doctor dear!" exclaimed the patient. "Things haven't changed at all—if anything, they're worse. Papa can't even sit up any more. It's definitely cancer of the intestines and they have decided not to operate. Of course Max had the very best men in consultation and they talked for a long time, learnedly, I suppose, in the front parlor downstairs. Max is very important at all these conferences. He dotes on them. And when they are over, he tells me explicitly just what the new doctor has ordered for Papa and what I must do. Then he forgets all about number 25 West until I call him up again to ask about the medicines or something."

"Did you get away at all, Rosalie? Did your sister take over part of the summer?" asked Dr. Ford quietly.

"No, somebody had to stay at home with Papa," she said wearily. "And Hilda went down to Elberon as usual, with Celia and Ralph. She said the children just couldn't stand the city heat. Besides it would have interfered with Hilda's social ambitions for Celia at the Beach Club if the Samuel T. Winters had not opened their cottage for one season. Oh, they'll be back tomorrow," continued the patient tartly.

"And how about your brother, Dr. Max?"

"Oh, Max couldn't come around often. He's on service at the Heights Hospital during August and during July he was covering some friend's practice. Then he had to run up to the Berkshires to see Henrietta and little Max and his other brat a couple of week-ends. And Forest Hills is so very, very far from New York," continued Rosalie sarcastically. "You know Max. He never has time to visit anyone but his patients."

"And that left Miss Rosalie Stein bravely holding the fort," said Ford sympathetically.

"Oh, Doctor," she burst forth, "that's what I think is so unfair. Just because I'm an old maid. It's always been that way and it rankles. First I was the girl and Max was a boy and older. Always the favorite. He had to have the new bicycle and I could keep my old dolly. And then I became the older, older than my little sister Hilda, who turned out to be so cute and smart from the day I first heard her cry. Not that I remember that. Very vaguely I do remember the doctor with a black bag going upstairs to Mama's room at 25 West and my nurse telling me the doctor had brought me a little sister. I must have been four then and from that day on it was always I who must be good to my cunning little sister. She was always the pretty one. Oh, Doctor, why was I born so very plain with stringy yellow hair and a long face and a thin bent nose. I detest myself for detesting myself but I detest Hilda and her brood, too. She is always talking about them."

Doctor Ford had reached for a pad on the desk in back of him. He took his glasses from a small leather case, adjusted them quickly, and began taking notes of Miss Stein's exact words. As the years passed he made less frequent and briefer notations—only when the patient's utterances seemed specifically significant or illustrative of some unusual mechanism of special interest in the psychoanalytic theory.

Miss Stein ceased talking, crossed her legs and lay immobile except for her rapid, shallow breathing. Ford observed her in silence and after a while said in his matter of fact tone,

"Let it come, Miss Stein."

"That simple truth which just slipped out has me tongue-tied—that I should wish Hilda's children should die. I don't know that that's so awful—but it's hard to think it about myself, the envious embittered creature I'm becoming," she cried softly in self-pity and took from her handbag, which lay on the couch beside her, a small, flowered linen hand-kerchief with which she dabbed her eyes. Then she smiled for a moment.

"It won't hurt me to come down from my pedestal. Some-times my hate of Max and Hilda is ill-disguised, I fear."

"And perhaps far more apparent to them than you sus-pect," added the doctor bluntly. "It may well be an element in your loneliness."

When Miss Stein said nothing, Dr. Ford again prodded her with his stereotyped query,

"What comes to your mind?"

"I hate to tell you, Doctor dear, but I met Willy Comstock one day quite by chance last summer when I was shopping. I hadn't seen her for ten years—not since that terrible Sunday afternoon when Papa and Mama told her never to come to 25 West again, never in all her life. You know all about that horrible Sunday afternoon when Papa surprised us together on the sofa in my room upstairs. I shiver whenever I think of it."

A long pause ensued and finally the patient continued reluctantly, "I am so ashamed to tell you after all the work you have done with me. Willy looked awfully old and shabby and seedy, but I must confess the old thrill did return to me when I saw her. Not the indifference I know that you would have wished, Doctor, and not an antipathy, which I think you might have preferred to my positive feelings of attraction. My heart beat fast when I spied her and I stammered when I spoke. I met her face to face so suddenly. She was as com-posed and self-possessed as ever—made a few casual inquiries about the family. I answered them all like a self-conscious little girl and then I fled feeling very stupid, but I was trem-bling like a leaf inside."

Suddenly and quite unconsciously she slipped her hands,

palms down, underneath her body and lay on them firmly as though this position would help keep them away from forbidden practices. She stayed perfectly still for several minutes before she burst forth again.

"Oh, Doctor dear, why did mother ever send me to Camp Winnesockett? Why did I have to meet Wilhelmina Comstock there? Why ever in my life? I am so lonely, so desperately lonely, and sometimes I still yearn for Willy. Isn't that despicable—with all my other troubles? Trouble, trouble, all my life I've had trouble. Sometimes I think even you can't help me. What shall I do? What can I do?"

"You needn't worry about it," said Ford in a soothing tone, attempting to reassure the quivering, panic-stricken woman but he felt his words lacked the resonant fullness of conviction. "Such setbacks as this must happen, do happen with every patient, especially those who, like yourself, have such a strong craving to be loved and may I say also to be admired. When you fail to get it from without, the only way to attain it, the easiest way, is to admire yourself. And so people like you become more self-centered than you are ever consciously aware. Even now I think you only partially admit this aspect of your character. You know, Rosalie, I once thought of writing a book about neuroses and neurotics. I had the title all picked. I intended to call it 'Dear Me'."

Rosalie Stein winced as though she had been pierced with a sharp instrument. Her face contorted as if in the anguish of physical pain when she cried out:

"Oh, Doctor, am I sick or am I just wicked?"

"Of course you are sick," answered Ford unequivocally, "although I must admit that perhaps a century ago few people would have considered your homosexual longings as an illness. Now we know that in many instances, like yours, they result from frustration of normal love impulses and take a devious side path when the broad open road to happiness has been blocked by fear."

Miss Rosalie Stein smiled fleetingly in momentary relief and then changed the topic.

"But things are so bad at 25 West. Father's so grumpy we can't get a nurse to stay most of the time. Besides Papa has become so frightfully stingy. He begrudges every penny, even for his own medicine."

"Well, you must know there is a severe depression on and a great many people are fearful of the future and are retrenching," interposed the doctor.

"Of course I know that. The big Bank of the United States failed. I am not as unworldly as all that. But I really don't believe that we have to be as careful and saving as Papa makes out. And I just can't stand the filthy smells of his disease. You know my morbid fears of dirt and disease. It's terrible to be chained to this job of nursing a crabby, sick old man. And then to have Willy turn up again, even if our meeting only stays a memory. It got me all stirred up again. Why did I ever submit to Willy's lure, Doctor dear. Will I ever get over it?"

"Do you mean your longing for Willy? I hope so, because it troubles you so much. But this is not the sole cause of your loneliness. You told me so often that you've been lonely as long as you can remember and that kind of loneliness may be due to an early deprivation of love. Just now I would say rather that you are lonesome not having anyone—Willy or Genevieve or that wholesome Norwegian girl you met on a North Cape cruise. There have been no intimacies with women since you began to see me, isn't that correct, Rosalie?"

"Oh, yes, it's absolutely true. But you know that's because I love you so very deeply, Doctor dear. But you yourself have told me so often that my feeling for you is not a true love, not a very healthy or natural love."

"Yes, that's so," confirmed Ford, using the opportunity to attempt again to weaken the overstrong adulation and dependency of the floundering grown-up girl. "After all, I probably represent only a good and considerate father, replacing the one who now on his deathbed is as little interested in your present trials and sacrifices for him as he was in your childhood troubles which were so important to you."

"Oh, Doctor," wailed Miss Stein, "all the loves I have ever had have been unhealthy—loving a woman like Willy, almost old enough to be my mother—she taking me for a lover. Yes, I suppose you're right. I suppose I did want to be like Max. Why shouldn't I? With all the fuss mother made over him, and her perpetual 'Rosalie, that isn't nice for little girls to do' which she said so solemnly and reproachfully. Especially the time when I innocently asked that little boy at dancing class to dance with me. The way she looked at me made me feel as though I had committed some unforgivable crime."

"And may have made you envy the little boy who had all the prerogatives and could ask whom he wished to invite with impunity," supplemented Ford as he bent forward to give emphasis to his remark.

"Maybe you're right, Doctor, maybe it is, as you explain, an identification, an emulation of the little boy, and a masculine protest and envy of that little thing the boys have—I can never use that word you call it. But of course, Doctor dear, I know you wouldn't say a word like that unless you had to," added the patient apologetically, as she turned her head to look back affectionately at the physician. "But I am so lonely and so trapped and so different. If I do get well, now that I am past forty, what chance have I got. It's too late—I'm on the shelf—oh, Doctor dear, there's no one but you."

"Your homosexuality is not the whole of your problem, Rosalie, as you must perceive. Some very successful people with friends and family who love them may suffer from this feeling of loneliness—artists, poets, even our late President Wilson whom you admire so much, have complained of it. If every unmarried woman and man were as unhappy as you—if every homosexual person were so miserable, it would indeed be an even far more troubled world," said the doctor with greater earnestness than usual, for the patient seemed desperate.

"But Doctor dear, Doctor Ben, I am captive. I am captive of Willy, of father, of Max, of Hilda—captive of myself. My vice is a vise which has kept me locked tight. Can you release me? I can't endure it much longer," cried the tortured girl as she squirmed where she lay.

"I will try to help you now as I've tried right along. We will try to work it out together," the doctor said quietly and with such sincerity that the patient responded.

"Yes, we will go on together and now I'll go back dutifully to father's dark, musty room at 25 West to wait for Hilda to bounce in for her first visit and then wait until the registry sends us a new nurse and wait 'til Max makes a formal professional inspection of the new nurse and impresses her with the fact that he once interned at Bayview Hospital and then I'll resume waiting for some visitors to call at 25 West. But thank God I can be a visitor, Doctor, pay a visit to you three times a week. Sometimes I think you are God and I pray to you like to God sometimes. Now I have told you!"

"Place not your faith in princes," said Ford simply. It was a pet reply of his whenever patients attempted to praise him extravagantly, to overestimate the potentialities of his method and his service.

"There is no shame in unrequited love, my mind tells me that," murmured the whimpering patient, "but something inside me makes me feel guilty about it."

"Perhaps the guilt stems from other sources—from the feeling that you should not attempt to love in some of the ways you do—Willy, for instance, and also your own self so very dearly."

"Oh yes," agreed the patient so readily that the physician knew that her words were the empty acquiescence of a dutiful school-girl rather than the conviction of a thoughtful grown-up. Then she asked, "Have I come to rely on you too much? Whenever a difficult situation arises, I think I can come and tell you and it does not seem so bad. Do you think it will always be that way?"

"No, surely not. It's not good to depend on anyone that way. The feeling will grow weaker as you become stronger and more self-reliant."

"And so I'll go back to 25 West now," the patient said meekly as she stood before the doctor with a gracious but resigned smile transiently passing over her plain face. When she reached the door, she turned and seemed almost radiant as she said:

"It's life itself to have you back." Then she added an afterthought, "When you receive crumbs you're grateful, though that's hopeless in comparison with what I need—but dear Doctor, don't think I'm unappreciative."

After she had departed Dr. Ford shook his head in doubt. The dependency, the transference as he thought of it in psychoanalytic terminology, had persisted too strongly and too intently. He had been unable to decrease it with all the devices which he had tried, all the tools at his command. Also he was disturbed about the repeated recurrence of the phrase '25 West' with the omission of 79th Street. Merely a manner of speech perhaps, but such idiosyncrasies were apt to be significant. West was where the sun set, the boys in the war used the phrase 'going West' for dying. In her case a compulsive drive to 'go West' could appear should her faith in him to cure her be too greatly shaken by an unbearable pressure of outside events.

As he shifted his attention hour by hour to a new patient, Ford had thought of his position as akin to that of the chess master playing eight or ten boards simultaneously without confusing the pictures. To be sure his contests were always against opponents less skilled than himself and like the pro-

fessional chess player, in most instances, he was sure of victory
if he played each situation slowly and cautiously. The worst
result he could get would be an occasional stalemate or draw
—unless the patient, unable to accept defeat or even a draw,
should refuse to play further and petulantly sweep the chess-
men to the floor. And his disquieting thoughts reverted to
Miss Stein, so desperately in need of consolation and accept-
ance.

The dirty, ankle deep slush of a thawing February snow-
storm covered the city streets and a wind-swept sleet kept
everyone indoors near steaming radiators, unless the need
for leaving was really urgent. The rough weather did not prevent Rosalie Stein from appearing at the doctor's office precisely on time for her appointment. The wind and cold had
blown a slight tinge of pink into her thin cheeks. Her gray-
blue eyes sparkled again as she tripped into the office and
smiled almost gaily at the physician.

"A week is a dreadfully long time between visits, Doctor
dear," she began, "but it's all over now—father's long, lingering and torturous passing away, the funeral, with its melan-
choly service, Hilda's feigned grief, Max's officiousness as
head of the family, the bitterly cold ride to Brooklyn for the
burial. It's all a memory now and even the will has been
read."

"And your father did the right thing by you in the end?"
inquired the doctor continuing the strategy of emotional
support and conciliation which he had not dared allow to
lapse completely at any time since the patient had first
walked into his office nearly three years previously.

"Yes, he did," she said curtly, "all the insurance was in my
name and it's nearly $100,000 in all—and the rest of the
estate is to be divided equally in three parts. After the lawyer
had read the will, Hilda's abundant sorrow suddenly changed
into caustic comments, but the lawyer, Mr. Hiller, an old

friend of Papa's, paid no heed to her. He said he was entirely sure of father's intentions. So now I am free, free from the gloomy old house, free from father's miserliness, free from the mousy smells, free"—she faltered and choked, "but not free from myself."

"What do you intend to do?" asked the doctor in his professional voice, sliding back easily in his chair and relighting a cigar on which he puffed leisurely.

"For once Herman Stein's children are agreed. That horrible old house is to be sold, and the furniture is to be sold after each of us has taken what we wish. We had no more come to an agreement than Hilda began to collect some special things she fancied without so much as yea or nay to Max or me."

"And you, what do you intend to do?" repeated Ford.

"I've done it already. This time I made my own decision without asking anyone, not even you. I know you'll like my doing that, Doctor. This very morning I rented a two room apartment in the San Fernando, the new hotel on Central Park West, with a front room overlooking the Park. It's a stunning view. Aren't you proud of me, Doctor darling?" asked the patient turning her head appealing to the doctor.

"Yes, that's fine," he replied acquiescing to her need for approval.

"And I'll furnish it with some of the more recent things from 25 West," she continued, "but most of it will be new and shining and bright-hued and I'll have a home of my own and visitors. I've been so lonely. But, Doctor dear, who will the visitors be? I have been in prison so long." She began suddenly to weep. "Willy is my only friend, my enemy is my only friend, but I won't have Willy either, I promise you, it wouldn't be fair to you. But who will come? No visitors ever came to 25 West. Now surely Hilda and Max will visit me, don't you think, Doctor, but who else?"

"Oh, you'll pick up new threads of life gradually," encouraged the doctor. "Hilda and Max will help you. There will be some friends, new interests, you will renew your former devotion to music and you're in a position to travel a bit. And now that you have been relieved of the burden of your father, why don't you take up some work you really like. You have a talent for weaving. Why not see if you cannot help teaching the blind. Such places as the Lighthouse for the Blind can always use volunteers who are skilled and reliable."

"That last won't do at all—at least not now. Later maybe. For the moment I want to live for myself and not be confined by anyone, to anything, least of all to depressing, handicapped people like the blind. I don't want to do anything unless someone would say, 'Please do it for my sake' ", replied Miss Stein irritably, sharply and impatiently as she turned away from the doctor and started for the door.

The voice which so often reveals what words attempt to conceal did not escape the doctor and worried him. The patient showed no sign of being willing to diminish her demands upon him. He knew, too, that he would never be able to fully satisfy these childhood cravings and needs which with all his help she seemed unable to abandon. What was far more dangerous, he realized, was that when the patient came fully to appreciate this, she might, probably would, become hostile, vindictive and maybe revengeful towards him. It was an old story which he knew from experience—ever increasing, insatiable demands for attention and approbation on the part of the patient in the face of sexual frustration for reassurances over and over that he or she was without question the doctor's favorite child.

Miss Rosalie Stein stared out at the inspiring sight below her window where spring had come to spread its temporary green mantle over the park, but to her everything seemed as hopeless as ever. At her back was her own living room looking fresh and crisp, just as she had so often dreamed it—adjoining it her bedroom, white, immaculate, depressingly still. Yet everything seemed so futile. Two months had passed since she was prepared to receive visitors. She had announced triumphantly to Hilda and Max that she was ready for company and would like them to come. Once indeed Hilda had rushed in on her way to luncheon at Longchamps with an acquaintance from Long Branch. She was terribly sorry she could not ask Rosalie to come along, but it was Mrs. Schneider's invitation. The apartment was 'just too sweet for words,' and the 'Dresden clock I've always wanted looks just too darling on your bureau'.

Miss Rosalie Stein returned wearily into her bedroom. She was startled when she looked at the delicate, flowered, white Dresden clock ticking quietly. It was already ten o'clock—she must have been staring out of the window for an hour. She began to move quickly, but with effort. She must keep her eleven o'clock appointment with the doctor. It was Friday and none would follow for three days. Later, as she lay curled up on the couch in the doctor's office, Miss Stein rattled off her troubles and slights tearfully and with nervous urgency as she had time and again before.

Her words flowed in a continuous, meandering stream. Ford stifled a yawn and allowed his mind to idle as he often did when listening to repetitions. He thought of himself like a prospector for gold, standing for long hours in a mountain stream looking for grains of gold among the shale and slate which mostly flowed into the pan. Like the man seeking gold, who becomes attentive when he catches the glitter of small particles in the tumbling waters, so the physician through a change in the position, expression, coloring or inflection of the patient's voice receives a warning when some more important material is likely to appear in the stream of thoughts flowing from the mysterious depths of the mind.

Now Miss Stein's eyelids fluttered, her muscles began to twitch first in her eyes, then in her arms, then a convulsive movement of the abdominal muscles. She said in a muffled voice:

"Doctor dear, I am so humiliated. I don't believe I can endure it much longer. Hilda asked me to supper last night —the first time since the funeral. It was such a pleasant surprise for me. There were six, and everything seemed the way I'd pictured it—easy conversation, a well-prepared dinner, and a little fun. Then toward the end of the meal, a Mrs. Schapiro said in such an artificially courteous way to Hilda, 'I'm so disappointed Mr. Schapiro couldn't come this evening. You know it's his busy season and all the buyers are on. But he said that on account of the Depression, business is so rotten that he had to take out a customer to dinner and a show tonight to sell him just a piker bill of goods'. Oh, Doctor, the only time she has asked me in a year—to fill in." Miss Stein sobbed uncontrollably like a deeply wounded and insulted child hungering for love.

At various times Ford had thought of speaking with Dr. Max Stein to ask him and his sister, Hilda, to be more considerate and attentive to Rosalie. If they showed her more affection it might attenuate and dissipate the intense dependency and love with which she had invested him. Indeed from time to time she had spoken of her brother with the same zealous regard, something just short of passion, that she expressed for Ford. But Ford decided against the idea. Experience had taught him that forced attention cannot replace true affection and that when interest does not come spontaneously it is quickly discerned by the person who regards it as patronage. When he had once intimated to Miss Stein that he might like to broach the subject of his neglect and indifference to her brother, she became furiously incensed and indignant.

Ford thought it best to allow the emotional outburst to

exhaust itself. After perhaps a quarter of an hour of weeping she became relaxed and composed and continued to talk freely:

"And Max has not been to visit me either, but now he has promised to come with Henrietta for dinner tomorrow evening. I have it all planned. A wonderful lobster salad with a special mayonnaise, made just the way Max likes it. I'm so lonely and I always live in fear that he will 'phone at the last minute and make some excuse for not coming—a very sick patient as a rule. I dread it. If he disappoints me this time I can tell you, Doctor, that some day my brother is going to visit me," she said forlornly. Then turning a tear-stained, red-eyed face towards the physician, she said, "I've had enough for today, I'm very tired and jittery, Doctor dear. You have been very kind and patient with me, who always wants encouragement and makes such demands on your moral strength. I'll talk more about it when I come to see you on Monday."

Sunday morning at ten o'clock Dr. Ford's residential 'phone rang.

"Is this Doctor Benjamin Ford?"

"Yes."

"This is Walter Hall, the manager of the San Fernando Hotel. When the maid went to the apartment of Miss Rosalie Stein this morning, she found she had died during the night."

"You don't say," murmured Ford, startled but immediately suspecting the cause. "What happened?"

"Suicide, I should say. I went up to the room. Everything was in order. I found her lying on the bed, dressed in a cream lace dress. There was an empty bottle of luminal beside her bed. She left a sealed note addressed to you. What shall I do? Will you come up?"

Doctor Ford reflected for a moment. Then he said in an

unruffled voice, "Would you be good enough to call her brother, Dr. Max Stein, in Forest Hills. He will take charge."

Ford replaced the receiver very slowly on its base, then he sank into a chair with a sense of defeat, tired out with the sudden fatigue of one who has been vanquished in a long, tedious struggle.

"Well," he said almost inaudibly, "this time poor Rosalie Stein won't be disappointed—she will have her brother visit her at last."

VIII

GALLANT FATHER

After a slow, hot train ride from Genoa, Dr. Ford had arrived at the Hotel Martinez on the Croisette at Cannes. All the same, he thought, it must be something extremely urgent that made Dr. Nichols send that radiogram to the ship, thus interrupting his journey and changing all his plans. The message had been put into his hands only half an hour before the Patria reached Genoa. He had been looking forward to a leisurely journey through Switzerland and to arriving in Paris in time to meet Smitty later. And now he was here in Cannes to see Nichols' patient—doubtless an over-indulged young lady who had had the misfortune—or maybe the convenience—to become sick on her honeymoon. He remembered that Nichols had mentioned her name, Mrs. Ronald Stewart, Frederick McMurtry's daughter. Her husband, young Stewart, had come to the station to motor Nichols to the hotel where his bride lay ill. He was in his early twenties, an exceedingly thin, blond fellow and not too robust looking.

Some rich men, like Fred McMurtry, could at times be most inconsiderate. Perhaps he had been merely self-important, radioing the ship from Texas, interrupting Dr. Nichols' and now his own plans and spoiling a much-needed holiday. "My daughter Mrs. Ronald Stewart dangerously ill Hotel Martinez Cannes. Will you attend her at once." Possibly the old fellow was genuinely but unduly alarmed. Nevertheless, Nichols had displayed the radiogram to Dr. Ford with no little pride before disembarking at Villefranche. His vanity had been touched, just as Ford's vanity

150

in turn had been tapped by Nichols' subsequent radio from Cannes. "Would like to consult you about my patient. Good train connections Genoa-Cannes. Wire reply."

Still, it was a queer thing, thought Ford, as he mounted the steps of the hotel and picked his way through a crowd of elegant loungers, this business of Nichols' having asked him to make a special detour just to have a look at the patient.

Dr. Nichols was waiting in the lobby and as Ford came through the door he darted forward.

"I'm so glad you have come, Ford," he said as they shook hands. His face as well as his brief greeting showed his concern. "It goes without saying I wouldn't have asked such a favor of you except in a really serious case. This one has got me, almost. I'm puzzled. And it just occurred to me that a sensible psychiatrist, such as you, might be of help. Come up to my room and I'll tell you the details about the patient—one of the strangest cases in my experience."

Dr. Nichols' room faced the bay. Cap d'Antibes lay on the horizon, a gleaming strip on the dazzling blue of the sea where boats with many-hued sails skimmed the waters.

"Take a chair," said Nichols, pushing forward a comfortable chintz-covered armchair. "And I've saved one of my precious Coronas for you," he added as he offered Ford a large foil-wrapped cigar.

As Nichols talked, he walked up and down. "Mrs. Stewart," he said, "is in a very bad condition. She is vomiting her head off. She's been married just three months—is on her honeymoon—and supposedly two months pregnant. At least, the French doctor and an English doctor they called in here think she may be."

"Where do I fit in?" asked Ford.

"Just wait and you'll see. For one thing, I felt the need to talk the situation over with someone who speaks my language. The French doctor may be all right. He *'mon*

confrère's' me obsequiously, but I suspect he doesn't think
that an American doctor can know any medicine and doesn't
want me on the case. And that blasted Englishman just
stands there stiffly and stares blankly at me, repeating 'quite
so, quite so, quite,' whether I say yea or nay. They're damn
disconcerting, these Englishmen! The point is, I can't find
any real signs of pregnancy. But I'm in charge of this case
from now on. The other two doctors will come to see the
patient only if and when Bill Nichols asks them to—even if
they lock me up for practicing medicine in France without a
license. McMurtry has wired me to assume full responsibility.
Let's get back to the facts of the case. Louise—that's Mrs.
Stewart—a stunning girl, made her debut in New York society two years ago, with great success and too much pub-
licity. She is the apple of her father's eye. If we can do
anything to save her, Ford, we've got to act quick."

"But where does a psychiatrist come in?" asked Ford, still
wondering why he had been asked in consultation.

"You'll see in a minute. The young woman acts strangely.
Take, for instance, those dark blue velvet bowknots she
wears on all her clothes. . . ."

"Bowknots?" asked Ford, with his first show of interest.

"Yes. It's an odd idiosyncrasy. She wears one on all her
negligees and gowns, and when once out of curiosity, I
touched the bowknot resting on her bosom she got wildly
excited and begged me not to remove it. I hadn't, of course,
the least intention of doing so. This girl is about twenty-
one—and very beautiful as she lies there in her sheer trous-
seau gowns of palest pink. Yes, those bowknots she pins on
her clothes certainly seem queer to me, though, Lord knows,
I don't pretend to be a psychiatrist. Then, the way she stares
out of the window, as if seeing visionary things. There are
no signs of pregnancy so far as I can make out, but she has
missed a period, has morning nausea, and suffers from that
uncontrollable vomiting."

"The blue bowknots do sound unusual, perhaps abnormal. You may be right, the case may be in my field," replied Ford, whose mind had begun to speculate on the psychological possibilities. "How long has she been vomiting?"

"For over a month now. Ever since they arrived at the Riviera. Dr. Duval, the Frenchman, has tried all sorts of bland diets and all the combinations of bismuth and even morphine. She is thin as a rail and alarmingly weak. Her father, who seems to be extremely attentive, has wired his intention of coming over from Houston. He may arrive in a few days."

"You said her father is absolutely devoted to her, didn't you?"

"Oh, she is McMurtry's only child and he has been very proud of her. A more attentive father I have never seen."

"What about the young husband?" inquired Ford, as he slowly unwrapped the foil from the expensive cigar.

"Devoted, and wholly in love with her—as she apparently is with him. Well, shall we go to see the patient, Ford?"

The Stewarts' suite was on the same floor. Ronald Stewart opened the door to them, a stoutish, blond young man, in the early twenties. He had changed his dress to Riviera style —maroon linen trousers, blue sports coat and a white linen, open neck shirt. The costume seemed incongruous to his manner. He appeared anxious, uncertain of himself, a bit apologetic, and helpless as he greeted the doctors. His blue eyes, always watery, filled with tears as he said in his ingratiating, wavering voice, "You can save her, Dr. Nichols. I know you'll save her."

Nichols introduced Ford and they spoke briefly with the soft young man. A red-cheeked English nurse, a hearty middle-aged woman, was wiping the prostrated girl's lips lightly with moistened gauze.

"How's the patient, Sister?" asked Nichols professionally.

"No change, Doctor. She's had another fit of throwing up a

few minutes ago, although I gave her only Vichy and milk. Now she's lying there limp and merely staring ahead."

The large, high-ceilinged room was bathed in light, reflected from sea and sky, which entered through tall windows facing on the broad avenue in front of the hotel. Outside, palm trees rattled their dry dentated leaves in the gentle breeze which stirred the muslin curtains. Within, the clean delicate odor of verbena filled the room. In a wide bed, motionless, with her chestnut hair spread out over the ample pillow, her face as white as the linen itself, lay Louise. Hearing them come in, she opened her eyes languidly and smiled feebly. She seemed too weak even to extend her hand which was lying at her side as Nichols presented Ford.

"Louise," said Nichols quietly, "this is Dr. Ford, an American doctor—someone from back home. Won't you talk with him a little? I thought he might be able to help you. You seem so worried—and that's Dr. Ford's specialty—helping folks who are troubled."

Folded over a chair next to the bed lay a pale yellow negligee. Pinned to its wide soft collar, a bowknot of stiff dark blue velvet made an incongruous contrast with the softness and delicacy of the robe. It matched almost exactly the blue-black velvet bow attached to the patient's nightgown. The two ends lay flat on her white bosom, reminding Ford disagreeably of a mourning crepe bow on a white door.

It is strange how a tragic image may remain fixed in the mind. Almost a week had passed and Ford was in Paris on a crowded cafe terrace. Suddenly as he sat there waiting for friends to arrive, the memory of his visit to Louise Stewart began to recur. What association had brought it up so clearly? Ah, yes, of course. The couple at the adjoining table.

There sat a prosperous looking, portly, elderly man, spruce and alert, much preoccupied with his feminine vis-à-vis—a young, vivacious woman certainly not more than half his age.

"A penny for your thoughts!" boomed a convivial American voice behind Ford as a plump, white hand was laid heavily upon his shoulder.

"Tubby Goodrich!" said Ford, hailing his college friend. "Sometimes people are willing to pay more than that for them, old fellow," he laughed jokingly.

A waiter hovered nearby. Tubby insisted on ordering drinks although his flushed face, slightly slurred speech and explosive manner indicated that he already had taken sufficient.

"Where'sh your friend, Dr. Nasmyth?" he asked.

"I left him at the Astoria where we're staying. He said he'd be here 'toot sweet'!"

"So you didn't come over on shame boat after all. How's that," Tubby wanted to know.

"No," said Ford, "Smitty canceled his passage at the last minute. Another emergency operation and on no less a person than the President of St. James' Hospital. He was not doing so well and Smitty wanted to stay to see him out of danger. As a matter of fact, though, we both arrived today in Paris. Smitty took a fast boat, the Europa."

"And you came over on shat ol' tub, Patria. Shat's a long way round. Did you go from Genoa to Lucerne?"

"No. I went right to Cannes. A doctor friend wanted me there in consultation in a most interesting case."

"Oh, you medicos and your hospitals!" scoffed Tubby, signaling the waiter again. "Nozzer martini—*un bock* for my friend," he said in unmistakable American French.

"Well, as for me," Tubby went on, "I'm on what looksh like a holiday for life. Things been goin' from bad to worsh for American Motors. I haven't had a damn thing to do in six months. Let me tell you, France ish going to hell. Just damn fools to let Hitler take she Rhine. Boch'll be in Paris

in five years. But we'll let zat pass. How you like jis place?
Rond Point. What you say ol' fellow. *Très, très jolie.*"

Tubby's French was directed to a passing girl who ignored
him and proceeded rapidly along the pavement with sharp
heel-taps. Possibly she didn't have a taste for an older man,
thought Ford. Tubby showed his age lamentably. He had
become far too puffy and soft. To Ford's professional eye,
this meant too much alcohol and rich food.

They sat watching the passing crowd, enjoying the play of
the fountains which caught the setting sun's rays in little
rainbows. Nowhere except in Paris, thought Ford, could one
find such a sense of restfulness amid moving throngs of
people.

"Now this is just right," said Nasmyth's voice, as he appeared unobserved before them at their marble-topped table
on the awninged terrace.

"Hello, Smitty," said Ford casually, but he rose. "Tubby,
this is Doctor Nasmyth; call him Smitty, my good friend
and frankest critic. He keeps me from going out of bounds
—only psychiatrically of course."

"Shen you'sh a real benefactor of mankind," roared Tubby
extending his hand. "Sure glad t' meet'sh. Heard a lot
about'sh."

As they resumed their seats, Ford took a quick side-glance
at Smitty. He was worried about him. That sharp pain in
the left shoulder to which Smitty had confessed six months
ago had been followed by a brief but acute collapse. Smitty,
like any storekeeper or broker, had dismissed it carelessly as
"indigestion", but clearly, Ford thought, the overworked
heart had set up a signal of distress.

"Sorry to be late," said Smitty, "but I must have lingered
longer than I thought enjoying the Arc de Triomphe up the
slope and the obelisk of the Concorde down the other way.
Nothing like it in the world," he mused. "I thought that I
would never want to be in Paris again," he sighed, with a

sad look. Ford knew that his friend was thinking of the trip that he had made with Mrs. Nasmyth just before she had died in France seven years ago.

A query from Tubby interrupted their thoughts. "Martini?" he asked of Nasmyth.

"No, a brandy-soda."

And Tubby, on his fourth cocktail, ordered a new round of drinks. The three men settled down for a free conversation of friends without care.

"Whom do you think I met on the Europa?" Smitty asked.

"I'll bite," said Ford.

"Remember the old *Pschorr-Bräu* in Munich—God, it must be twenty-five years ago—well, Doctor Christopher Moore. Chris Moore was on the boat. He enquired for you, Benny. Remember his Tyrolean hat and those yellow gloves?"

"As if I could forget! What's he doing now?"

"Practicing physiotherapy in Cleveland. Diathermy cures everything from neurosis to empyema. Suite up on A deck. Big as a balloon. Wants to see Paris with us the right way if he can shake the wife and kids, and I suspect he'll manage it. I told him to call us up at the Astoria."

"Shee here, you fellas," said Tubby, his moon-like face flushed and his eyes slightly incoordinate, "I'm the one gonna show you gay Paree t'night. Wife and two boys down at Cabourg for sh' monsh. An' I know sh' hot spots."

"You're on," said Smitty agreeably. "If Chris Moore shows up there'll be four of us."

Ford turned to Nasmyth. "Well, now you guess whom I met on the Patria? No other than your friend, Dr. Nichols, internist at St. James."

"Bill Nichols!" said Smitty. "I didn't know he'd come over. What's he doing?"

"Well, on the strength of your friendship, we hit it off pretty well. We spent a lot of time in the smoking room, with Bauer, a gynecologist from St. Louis, swapping yarns. Then Nichols received a radio message from McMurtry, the oil millionaire, asking him to see his daughter who was very ill in Cannes."

"Old Fred McMurtry!" exclaimed Tubby who sat sprawling on his chair. "Presh'dent of the Un'vershal Oil Company, Benny? Tha's a good number—shol' boy and me an' a coupla ozzer fellas did Paris together coupla years ago—shom booze hound, Freddy! An' shom sheik wi' women over here."

"So I've been told," said Ford, suddenly slipping into his habitually professional reserve. "Well, as I was saying, Nichols got off at Villefranche. Then he telegraphed me to join him in Cannes. That's how I came to see the patient . . ."

"Oh, if you two fellash are goin' to talk med'shin again I'm goin' take a lit walk," said Tubby. "Shee wha's doin' downstairs in she lounge." He lumbered off and disappeared indoors.

"How long were you at the bedside of this apparently so puzzling patient?" asked Smitty.

"I stayed five days. And I left her in a much better condition than I found her," Ford said, not without a hint of professional pride.

"Yes," he went on, "and I think I left your colleague, Nichols, a little more respectful of psychiatry and its methods than he was when I first talked with him in the smoking room of the Patria."

"Tell me about the case," said Smitty. "And don't pretend you're not aching to!"

"I don't think that I can," Ford answered, "since you know who the patient is."

"I'm surprised at you, Benny," said Smitty somewhat offended. "Not only is this a professional discussion but you should know, after thirty years, that you can trust me implicitly about anything."

"Okay, then, and don't think I mistrust you. She had plenty of acute abdominal symptoms and that ought to cock your surgical ears—and don't pretend you're not itching to hear about it," retorted Ford. They had their glasses filled and Ford laid the groundwork for his story.

"So there she was," he said, summing up his first impressions, "a delicately featured, beautiful girl, lying in her big bed, so weak from lack of food she could scarcely talk—there was something ethereal in her beauty."

"And young, pretty rich, and newly-wedded to a man who loves her," mused Smitty, recapitulating. "On her wedding trip, and apparently dying of a mysterious illness. Not pregnant, yet vomiting day and night. And you say that in five days you left her better than you found her—on the road to recovery, I gather. Quite a mystery, eh Benny! What was back of it?"

"Well," Ford resumed, encouraged by his sympathetic listener, for the case still fascinated him, "that first day I didn't accomplish much. After a little random irrelevant probing I sat there beside her bed in silence. You know that waiting technique of ours. At last she said, hesitating, as though she could scarcely permit the words to cross her lips, 'Am I going to die, Doctor? I feel so feeble. And I don't want to die, I want to live—I'm so young, and I love my husband!' With that she fell to sobbing.

"I watched her. Instead of turning toward me, to look for reassurance, as most patients do when they ask that question of a physician, Louise's gaze wandered to the French windows and the dazzling blue southern sky. I sat there patiently. She stopped sobbing presently, but moved restlessly in bed, turning her head repeatedly towards the window. It was a movement I had observed before in patients lying on the couch in my office when they had been talking or merely thinking of suicide."

"But I understood you to say this girl wanted to live! She wasn't depressed, was she?" asked Smitty.

"No. Just resigned. The situation here demanded a quick relief of symptoms—otherwise she might really die of exhaustion."

"You're not telling me anything there," added Smitty understandingly. "I've had a few such cases on my own surgical ward. I'll never forget one who developed hiccoughs after an operation which we couldn't stop. He passed out in nine days of sheer collapse. Hiccoughed himself to death."

"Well," Ford went on, "after my first visit to the sick girl I took a walk all alone along the beach, as far away as I could get from that crowd of wanton wasters who hang out around all the fashionable hotels in Cannes. I wanted to do a little thinking. As you know, I haven't practiced hypnosis for some time, but we used to do it in the early days at the Cornell Clinic twenty years ago. I once cured a young fellow of stammering—by suggestion. Cured him for a few days, you know, until he relapsed. But I discarded hypnosis when I began to understand Freud and why he himself abandoned it so many years ago."

"What's the matter with hypnosis anyway, Benny?"

"Well, nothing and everything. Nothing because some times you can get marvelous and quick relief of symptoms of pains in the head and feet; you can make people walk who thought they were paralyzed; others to see again who thought they were blind. Just like at Lourdes."

"And what's wrong with it then", repeated Smitty.

"Just that. Just like Lourdes. You don't know why it happened or what happened and as a rule they don't stay cured for long. Also not too many people can be completely hypnotized, and only too often those who can be put under deep hypnosis are the kind who will make no effort to help themselves. They want to throw themselves under the control and direction of some one stronger than they are and stay there."

"I think I get it", said Smitty. "The doctor encourages

them in their weaknesses when he takes over complete control."

"Something like that", said Ford. "Anyway, after mulling over the situation at Cannes in my mind I came to the conclusion that because of the desperate state of the girl, I'd try it. The clue to the whole thing might be, I thought, in that remark Nichols had let drop about Louise's attentive father."

Smitty took from his pocket a yellow pack of cigarettes labelled Cigarettes Français—Maryland. "I always buy these stinking black weeds when I'm here—rather have them than the best Egyptians. What good would knowing about her father do?"

"Early emotional attachments of children to their parents or parent-images—often undeniably incestuous—become deeply unconscious in their minds. This repression happens because of our cultural taboos and the conscious effect of these repressed feelings upon the individual may not be too obvious. Nonetheless their unconscious influence may continue to operate powerfully, especially in their love affairs."

Two young women in decollete summer dresses passed slowly by, pausing to glance at the people on the cafe terrace, as if waiting to be invited in. Then they moved on, giggling.

"Did you notice?" said Smitty. "Those two gave us old guys the glad eye!"

"Yes, and the incident is amusingly relevant, for it bears quite directly on the case I was telling you about," said Ford.

"You amaze me, Holmes," said Smitty jestingly. "I must really have the mentality of a Watson, for I don't see the point. But go on."

"Well, as I was saying, I decided to use hypnosis on Louise and to use the authoritative technique to induce sleep—forcefully to command her to fix her attention on me. That would be in line with the ideas of Ferenczi—I may have told you about him—that Hungarian who came to the U.S.A. with Freud in 1909. So, when I returned to see the patient the morning after my solitary walk, I had my plan mapped out. The English Sister reported that Louise had not vomited, but had slept fitfully and muttered a great deal in her sleep. The nurse had not been able to understand the words. 'It was a mixture,' she said, 'of English and French, but I cawn't say really which, Sir."

"Did Fred McMurtry's daughter speak French fluently enough to dream in it?" Smitty wanted to know.

"Pretty good for you, you're improving," exclaimed Ford smiling. "She had had a French governess most of the time as a child. That second morning, Louise again barely greeted me as I sat down beside her bed and took hold of her hand. She didn't speak, but now and then I felt a soft pressure of her fingers against mine. Her sweetness and pathetic helplessness were very childlike as she lay there. I interpreted them as an unconscious appeal for love and I decided not to use the commanding method, after all, but to hypnotize the girl by softly lulling her to sleep. I told her what I was going to do. The English Sister looked at me sceptically but was too well trained to make any comment when I asked her to go into the sitting room and leave me alone with the patient."

"Always hypnotize with no one around, Benny?" asked Smitty.

"It seems to work a little better that way—at least with me and especially when it's the first attempt. At all events, after I stroked Louise's brow many times, murmuring suggestions of drowsiness and sleep, monotonously over and over again, she fell into a mild hypnotic state.

"After a while, following the earlier clue she had given me, I suggested that she tell me what she saw outside the window. Presently, in a voice low and expressionless, Louise began:

'I'm a little girl six years old and I'm standing on a balcony overlooking blue water and a road. There are open French windows behind me. My French governess is there inside the room. Now I see a carriage far down the road. It's drawn by a prancing black horse. It comes nearer and nearer. I see a pretty lady sitting in it, all dressed in white lace, and she is holding a white lace parasol over her head. She is lovely— the prettiest lady I ever saw.'

"At this point Louise seemed about to wake, so I stroked her brow again and crooned several times, you're getting drowsy, oh so drowsy, drowsy, drowsy, drowsier and drowsier. You're going to sleep. Almost immediately she fell off into hypnotic sleep again and began once more to speak quickly and animatedly. '*Mademoiselle* comes out on to the balcony with me,' she said, 'she sees the lady, too. *"Mon Dieu!"* she exclaims. Then she rushes back into the room and calls to my mother, *"C'est elle! C'est elle!"* Her voice is shrill with excitement. My mother comes to the balcony. She is fat and looks frowsy and I feel upset by her ugliness. She shakes her fist at the lady in the carriage. Mademoiselle keeps shouting, *"C'est elle, c'est elle!"* And Mother cries out, "The bitch! The bitch!"'

"With a piercing shriek Louise came out of her semi-hypnotic state clutching my hand frantically. At the sound of the scream the terrified English nurse hurried in from the next room. I reassured her with a glance and kept stroking Louise slowly and gently on the shoulder to soothe her. The girl sank back into her pillow, completely spent by a great emotional upheaval. Gradually a faint color began to return to her cheeks."

Smitty had been listening intently with a perplexed look on his face.

"What did you make out of all that talk?" he inquired.

"Do you begin to see a light?" asked Ford.

"No, not yet, Mr. Holmes," replied Smitty, becoming facetious to relieve his own tension. "But I am really interested in your amazing adventure."

"Well, then, Dr. Watson," Dr. Ford went on, "I let the patient rest for nearly a quarter of an hour. I inquired about this vision she had had. She could remember it only very vaguely, but to me it had been a significant revelation. I began questioning her about her father in the hope of awakening memories of him when she was a little girl, groping my way, touching lightly at points which might lead to new facts.

"Eventually she said, 'Father is a very gallant man—gay and lavish'. Then she continued to speak flowingly as though her tongue had been freed by the hypnotic experience. 'So liked by everyone. When he wanted anything he went after it and got it. He always adored me, and still does. He could get my moods before I knew them myself—and he was so capable of adapting himself to them. I couldn't imagine the world without father—absent people are not very far away if you love them'.

"Her eyes were gentle and wide, and her voice had become tender. Again I waited, though I felt I had learned important facts more quickly than I had expected . . . And I suppose you, first assistant," Ford concluded, smiling at Smitty, "have also by now made your own interpretation." Ford leaned back in his chair and looked towards the door of the café. "I wonder where Tubby is," he said.

"Skip Tubby until you've unravelled the mystery," said Smitty. "But hold on a minute. I think I am getting something. I suppose the pretty lady was old McMurtry's mistress?"

"Elementary, my dear Watson. Together we'll make a fine pair of amateur medical detectives. But, after that, what?"

"I defer to your superior skill, Holmes."

"But there, dear Watson, I have the advantage of you.

After her disclosure, Louise cried a little, glancing from time to time out of the windows. I then began questioning her for more than an hour, using as much tact and caution as I had. It was clear to me that the moment on the balcony she had described under hypnosis had been a determining one in her childhood. The mother, who was irritable and querulous, and neglectful of her appearance, seemed repulsive to the child as compared with the beautiful lady in the victoria. Far from blaming her father for his choice, she approved his discarding her own dowdy, untidy mother: the fair lady became a kind of ideal for her to emulate so as to gain her father's favor."

"You amaze me, Mr. Holmes," cried Smitty, "But now I no longer need your aid. What you're trying to say is that this beautiful, delicate, carefully nurtured American girl unconsciously wanted to be a 'pretty lady' and not a mother."

"Commonplace again, my dear Watson," remarked Ford. "Yes. Marriage meant ugly motherhood to her. Her vomiting was an unconscious protest against even the thought of it."

"But what about those bowknots?"

"Well, again in the most elementary form, they were a protest, a protest against being like all the other refined girls of her set, whose dress and accessories always had to be just so. She was uncomfortable when everything matched in the feminine way and possibly also she resented being a conventional woman."

"Let me ask you something here," said Smitty. "Did you find out whether this idiosyncrasy about clothes was new or had she had it before she married?"

"Really quite a long-standing, often carefully concealed habit and sometimes very embarrassing to her. Because of her beauty and popularity she had been chosen as a bridesmaid by several of her friends and the bridesmaids always wore identical dresses. Louise made a very strong effort to conform, but could not bring herself to do so. She felt compelled to pin a blue bowknot on her dress—and what disturbed her more, the knot had to be visible. She tried to make it tiny and inconspicuous. Of course she had no idea of its significance but it caused her a great deal of suffering. She refused her last two invitations to be a bridesmaid because of this obsession to add something exceptional and not in keeping with the role."

"I think I understand," said Smitty. "Look, here comes your friend, Tubby, and under his own steam, too."

Tubby, no longer drunk, but beaming broadly, loomed up across the tables on the terrace. He was accompanied by a small, meticulously well-dressed French girl, and they paused to talk to some acquaintances at a distant table.

"As to the bowknots," continued Ford, "You may draw some further inferences from the fact that they were blue, and that two fairly long ribbons always dangled from a bulky knot which joined them . . ."

"I may be obtuse, Holmes, but I'm unable to see what they suggest."

"Well, as you know, pink is the color which signifies girl babies, and blue is for boys."

"More of your symbolism? What on earth did you determine from that?" asked Smitty with a grimace.

"Nothing in particular, maybe, yet every little movement has a meaning of its own, as the song in the old musical comedy, *The Pink Lady* goes. Every thought and feeling by some gesture may be shown. Remember it? And excuse my rudeness: but I noticed that you felt for your tie and gave a tug at the knot just now as I finished talking about Louise's idiosyncrasy. Were you reassuring yourself, Smitty?"

"Some phallic symbol, as usual, I suppose. You analysts drive a man to drink," said Smitty impatiently, as he motioned to the waiter to refill his glass.

"Without the benefits of Mr. Freud's symbolism, some people around here seem to be doing right well in that direction," retorted Ford. "Seriously, though, I rather suspected, when I noticed that all Louise's bowknots were dark blue in color, that in addition to not wishing to be a mother this exquisite, strikingly feminine creature also unconsciously did not wish to be a woman. Perhaps you will admit this wish to be a man might be a sequitur to her desire not to be a mother and bring about an identification with her gallant father whom everyone liked and who always got what he wanted?"

"And by the symbol she was unconsciously telling her secret to the world—is that what you are trying to say, Benny?"

"And which is apparently finally seeping through your thick surgeon's skull," nodded Ford, with a twinkle and a smile, as he raised his glass to his friend.

Twilight had begun to fall over the beautiful avenue and the converging tree-lined streets. Mellow lights appeared towards the Place de la Concorde, faint in the mist of the August evening.

And there was Tubby, at last, reaching their table with steady gait, followed by the shapely young Frenchwoman, in a demure grey dress with a saucy apology for a hat perched on the side of her sleek blue-black hair.

"This is Mademoiselle Claudette," said Tubby, introducing her. "My friends, Dr. Ford and Dr. Nasmyth . . ."

They sat down. "Claudette's been reforming me," said Tubby, placing an arm carelessly over the back of her chair. "I was just beating it for the bar to have a few more Martinis when I ran into Claudette here, a little old friend of mine, you know. She pulled me down to a table and began lecturing me. Made me order a bottle of Vichy while she took a grenadine. Now I'm sober as an American judge is supposed to be."

Claudette sat placidly, understanding only vaguely what Tubby said.

"*Méchant garçon,*" she put in, tapping Tubby's arm, and showing a set of glistening white teeth in a warm smile.

"*Quelle gamine,*" he said to her, explaining to his friends: "That means a good kid in American."

"She certainly looks it," agreed Smitty, regarding her with admiration.

"*Oui, oui. Moi,* good keed," giggled the child-like woman. "But ze Tubby, he dreenk too much—*comme tous les Américains,*" she added. Her voice had a soft musical swing.

"Sorry, but I'll have to leave you fellows now," said Tubby. "Another party tonight. August is my busy season for demonstrating gay Paree to the big boys of American Motors and an assortment of their affiliates from Detroit and Pittsburgh. But how about day after tomorrow? I'll be free then. Meet here at five o'clock?"

Smitty consulted his engagement book. "I'm going to be on the Left Bank all that afternoon," he said. "Suppose we all meet somewhere there instead—say at the Périgourdine?"

"Oh, zee Périgourdine!" exclaimed Claudette, clapping her hands. "Zey have *truffes*—how you say?"

"Famous for its truffles," said Tubby, with the pride of a man about town.

"Good. The Périgourdine, five o'clock," said Smitty, noting it down. "And Mademoiselle Claudette, of course, she will come too!"

"You bet she will," said Tubby, as he jovially made off with her.

"Before we go to supper," said Smitty, turning to Ford when they had gone, "will you clear up one or two unsolved points which still perplex me in the Stewart story? Then our gab-fest will be over—at least for a while. How did that girl down in Cannes come out?"

"Well, you see, it's been almost a week since I saw her. I forgot to say that I succeeded in hypnotizing her very lightly on a second occasion. I think it was the fourth time I saw her. Then I made the positive suggestion that the vomiting would cease, that she was strong and young and that she would get well. Since I left, Nichols has kept me posted by wire. She has entirely stopped vomiting and is taking solid food once more."

"Good work. Do you think she accepted your interpretation of her symptoms?"

"I didn't explain too much as she wasn't ready for it. So I can't really say—But we talked about many of her family's problems and only on one point was she particularly touchy. She would not tolerate the least criticism of her father. But I'm sure she became convinced that she is not going to have a baby. I think, too, that recalling and reliving the early scene and discussing it even so superficially with me has relieved her fears and anxiety about motherhood to some extent. But Nichols also mentioned in one telegram that old McMurtry arrived at Cannes the day after I left . . . and that leaves me a little in doubt as to how much my suggestive treatment is responsible for the improvement."

"Maybe that gallant father of hers effected the final cure," said Smitty mischievously.

"Maybe you've got something there, old kill-joy. Anyway, we can't minimize the influence of his presence in a temporary recovery like hers—but I think if I see her when we get back to the dear old U.S.A. it will be a long, stubborn, psychotherapeutic job to make her appreciate the joys and satisfactions of the mother-role."

"Do you think that the yearnings of the motherly woman and the lady of leisure are always opposite?" asked Smitty.

"I have some ideas about that," said Ford meditatively, "and they impinge upon this case. Psychoanalytic studies of prostitution are rare. You see, when psychiatrists are called to examine prostitutes, they usually find women who have been arrested and have shown other deviations while in court or in prison, such as drug addiction, alcoholism or feeble-mindedness."

"Yes," said Smitty, "I know a very estimable and kindly lady who has founded a home which cares for unmarried mothers. She tried to persuade me that all these girls, many of them prostitutes, were feebleminded. She became quite indignant when I suggested that mostly the feebleminded ones were brought there by the police or social workers, and the really clever ones enjoyed themselves in luxurious apartments on Park Avenue."

"Well, I am convinced that it is an image far removed from the mother and the motherly woman which is the attraction men, married and unmarried, find in prostitutes. In some cases it drives well-bred women secretly to envy prostitutes and fancy being like them. It's all part of the unconscious desire begun in childhood to please the father through sensual attractiveness."

"Figured that out all by yourself, Benny. Pretty smart, ain't we," bantered Smitty.

"Quit joshing, of course not," answered Ford curtly. "This theory is based upon the study of fantasies and dreams of men and women of different ages and types undergoing psychoanalysis. In many instances, such identifications cause fervid rivalry with the parent of the same sex and emotional immaturity is a part of the general psychological picture. Probably in some professional prostitutes these are the underlying unconscious determinants—aside from the more obvious economic and accidental factors."

"Okay, Professor, the hour's up," said Smitty, rising from his chair. "Come around some time and I'll take out one of your ribs without charging you."

As the two friends strolled down the Champs Elysees towards a restaurant near the Madeleine which Tubby had recommended, a solitary girl eyed them tentatively from the shadow of the rows of horse-chestnut trees.

"Well, Benny," said Smitty, "kidding aside, guess you saved that Stewart girl's life. I've seen one or two like her mysteriously pass out.

"But now, let us have your theory about *that* feature of city life," said he, nodding in the direction of the girl's retreating figure. And he mused, as if to himself, "that lovely, well-bred Stewart girl and that little Claudette are truly sisters under the skin."

"In early childhood may have been under the influence of identical psychological factors," interrupted Ford, "only, as you see, they managed them very differently."

IX

FATHER'S BABY GIRL

A Sequence To GALLANT FATHER

It suited Ford that Tubby had suggested the Left Bank for their rendezvous. Crooked medieval streets leading down to wide Seine bridges and the quays, eighteenth century roofs above which loom gray cathedral towers; curious little shops of the butcher, the baker and the barber, students in careless attire, bookstalls, the Sorbonne and the medical school—these things, the total of them, make Paris' Left Bank. Ford was pleased to renew his student-day love for and appreciation of old Paris as he sauntered slowly along, peering into the unpretentious but varied displays in small shop windows, past the spouting fountain of the Place St. Michel beside which flower women were selling bright-hued, late summer blossoms.

He had loitered briefly at one of the stalls on the quays of the Seine where he knew he could not expect to make one of those mythical finds of a rare old print which in stories about Paris can be bought for a few sous. Instead of idling over the tattered lithographs and obsolete wares at the stalls he had spent an hour at two second-hand shops he had visited on former trips and felt fully rewarded when he discovered a first edition of *Des Maladies Mentales* by E. Esquirol and a still rarer, paper-covered, thin booklet of steel engravings of certain types of the insane. It was dated 1837, lacking one year of being a century old, and was intended to illustrate the text of Esquirol's work. The book-dealer knew full well the value of the volumes and the willingness of Americans to pay. After becoming the proud owner of the two, Ford reluctantly turned away from these tempting collections and sauntered to the narrow terrace of La Périgourdine in anticipation of the truffles for which Tubby had said it was famous.

A few couples were enjoying the mild late afternoon air on the terrace, boxed in with hedges. Among them Ford spied Claudette and Smitty, the latter quite dazzling in a new silk tie with broad green and white stripes. They were sitting close together and seemed to be deep in conversation over a brandy and soda and an anisette.

"Hi, there," he said, "I hope I'm not intruding on your *tête-à-tête.*"

"Not at all; you arrive just in time to do some necessary interpreting," said Smitty. "Claudette's exhausted her English and I've come to the end of my Cooperstown French. Tubby's not turned up yet, and we're not at all disturbed by the absence of your bibulous friend. What's saw—a surgeon's saw—in French?"

"I suppose *scie—scie de chirurgien?*" said Ford, and signalled a waiter.

"*Oui, oui,* now I know"! said Claudette with a little cat-yawn.

"I've been boring our charming young friend here," said Smitty, "trying to tell her about how I spent my afternoon. Have been poking round for hours trying to find the shop of a surgical instrument maker whom Phillips of Johns Hopkins told me about. Finally located it on the second floor of a courtyard apartment. Talk about making a better mouse trap! I bought a collection of hand-wrought scalpels and saws that are beauties. I see you've been doing the quays. Any finds?"

"Check," countered Ford, grinning as he triumphantly exhibited his prized Esquirol engravings which Smitty examined with interest as Claudette climbing up to kneel on a chair peered over his shoulder.

"Oof," said she. "You mans. You ver' strange *touristes américains*. Why not see le musée de Louvre or ze Gallerie Lafayette or ze Père Lachaise?"

"She wants to take me with her to the Luxembourg Gallery tomorrow—can you make her out? Her approach is so unprofessional and so is her get-up—no rouge, not too much lipstick, no mascara. I can't understand her. And that has nothing to do with our language difficulties. Take her attitude towards Tubby, now. She likes him, I gather—understands his carefree ways—I surmise it may also be because he spends freely—but she holds him a little in contempt along with all Americans—it's always 'beesness and anozzer dreenk.' "

Claudette looked from one to the other of the men and laughed congenially. She patted Smitty's hand. He looked down, noticed her glass was empty, and suggested another cordial which she accepted smilingly.

"Pretty nice little girl," opined Smitty.

"Moi? Moi, une gamine . . . how do you say . . . good keed!"

Smitty was obviously stirred by her seductive gaze, her grace, her naturalness.

Just then a woman walked by on the sidewalk, her arm linked in that of a man past middle age. The couple could hardly pass unnoticed. The woman was under thirty, with gleaming blond hair. Her black dress had been fitted with expensive skill to her slim, supple figure, accentuating her height, which was slightly over that of her companion. He carried himself with an erect, dignified bearing, just short of pompousness, had a carefully trimmed grey Vandyke beard, and in his lapel buttonhole there was the rosette of the Légion d'Honneur. A young woman of elegance, an elderly man of importance; withal, a handsome couple.

The woman nodded slightly but very directly to Ford as she passed.

"Oh, you Benny! You seem to meet them everywhere," said Smitty with a laugh.

"Do you know Madame Fostaire, Monsieur?" exclaimed Claudette. "She is very elegant, no? A very elegant American lady. She is ze mistress of Monsieur René Lefevre, the gentleman she's with."

"René Lefevre, the celebrated editor?" asked Ford.

"*Oui,*" said Claudette, her eyes still lingering admiringly on the figures of the two who were crossing towards the bridge.

"Yes, I know her," said Ford guardedly. His face and voice had become non-committal, as was habitual with him when he met a patient or heard one of them discussed outside his office.

"Another of your failures, I suppose," jibed Smitty, recognizing the significance of Ford's suddenly impersonal manner.

"Right again, Smitty," replied Ford with good humor. "Her story makes a first-rate sequel and supplement to the Cannes case we were talking about at the Rond Point the other afternoon. If you would like to know about her I'll complete your education maybe, some time when we get back to New York."

"Well, shoot it now. I like to hear about women from you. Claudette certainly won't understand. She'll just gaze and sip that wretched stuff that smells like liquorice. As long as your errant Ithacan friend stays away, there's nothing to prevent my indulging you in the relaxation you like the most. Shoot", he said good-naturedly.

"Speaking of my favorite sport, as you would have it," observed Ford. "Very few people ever manage to get away from themselves on holidays. A few years ago I was on the little mountain train going from Chamonix to the Glacier of the Rhone. It afforded thrilling views of Mount Blanc. Yet, on the seat ahead of me were two Viennese business men in earnest discussion for the entire trip about the merits of the Tyrolean Hydro-electric stock, and in back of me sat two American matrons in a heated argument as to which of their friends, Mr. or Mrs. Bonner (Jim and Mabel) was most responsible for the divorce which had recently rocked Cedar Rapids and adjacent Iowa."

"Well, then, supposing we plunge in for our weekly dose of medical-mystery while we wait," said Smitty.

"I'm game and itching," laughed Ford, shifting his chair and tilting it back as if it had been the swivel chair in his office. Then, lighting one of his mild five cent American cigars, his favorites, he began.

"Now, my dear Watson," he said, musingly, "I am sure you must have noticed that our graceful lady had a metal plate in the right side of the skull."

"Prodigious, Holmes, and how did you deduct that?"

"Very simple, my dear fellow, second sight, of course," said Ford jocularly, "and also because a brief history of the lady happens to be in one of the more recent box files in my office."

"That self-possessed, charming creature one of your patients? You amaze me, Holmes, but the plate in her skull—surely you have not been trespassing upon my surgical field."

"Not yet, Smitty, though she had an operation performed for a suspected brain tumor. You see, at the time the lady complained of agonizing headaches which had lasted for over a year—customary surgical approach, you know."

"Naturally that operation was done before she became a patient of yours, Benny," said Smitty, with a twinkle in retaliation.

"Obviously, my dear Doctor," replied Ford ceremoniously. "You see, Smitty, she had become mentally confused, dull and drowsy and showed some changes in the discs of her eyes. A pretty good surgeon in Indianapolis undertook an exploratory operation on the skull."

"Then who was that dapper Frenchman with her? A famous editor here, you said. Is she divorced?"

"*Ah, oui,*" said Claudette, who had apparently been busily engaged in scanning the dress of each woman who passed. "I must go telephone," she announced, thoroughly disinterested in the conversation which excluded her, and rose to go inside.

"She'll be prinking and gossiping in there a good half hour," Ford prophesied, "and, I guess, consider herself well rid of us."

"Yes, a nice, tactful kid," approved Smitty, "let's get on with this case with a surgical slant."

"The surgical slant ends right here, and the pastor takes over after the general and his sword of might have wrought their havoc," retorted Ford. "I saw her only a few times, after all, when she poured forth her tragic life's history."

"I'm surprised, Benny. I know her name, aren't you afraid I'll blab," said Smitty a trifle maliciously.

"Oh, dry up. That's settled. Well, she came to me for advice, which I did not give her and which she did not really want. But I thought when she thanked me a bit too effusively at the end of her last visit that she would choose the course and role which she did. You know, they call Lefevre the bull dog in French political circles. By the way, I thought she looked well and happy as she passed, didn't you?"

"Very," replied Smitty. "But begin at the beginning now; who is this American woman, this Mrs. Foster, divorcee, now here in Paris? And how did she happen to get that metal plate in her skull? Why the devil don't you ever stick to your story, Benny!"

"Let's start again, then. And I guess I was wrong when I said we were through with surgery. Do you remember the case of Homer Sprague—it was front page news in the tabloids about ten years ago. He was fatally shot by a blonde Follies girl in a third-rate New York hotel. Well, Katherine is his daughter. You remember Sprague was divorced from his wife. He left his whole fortune, made in Indiana limestone, to his only daughter, Katherine. Well, that's Mrs. Foster."

"I'm damned," said Smitty. "As a matter of fact, I remember all the details of that affair. The bullet passed through the left chest grazing the heart. Bernard Hess had the case and decided not to operate and Sprague died. Occasionally the Sprague case still comes up in the Surgical Society when we discuss the problem of conservative treatment of heart wounds. I guess with the better methods of anesthesia today almost any one would decide to operate," explained Smitty.

"And the operation would be a great success and the poor man would die of pneumonia—is that right? You fellows don't have your failures live on to talk like some of our neurotics do, Smitty," smiled Ford, giving his friend a tap on the arm. "How typical of you and me, right through the years! To you, the famous case of Howard Sprague is the simple one of a heart grazed by a bullet and the surgical problem of whether or not to operate. To me, that part of it is merely the aftermath. What counts for me is what came before—the motivating details—the paradoxical factors which brought old Sprague and the hot-tempered show-girl together in the dingy hotel room. And those are things which you surgeons never bother about," said Ford, leaning forward to relight his cigar.

"You see, at the time of her father's murder and the subsequent scandal, Katherine was only about eighteen," he continued, settling back again. "She beat it straight from Indianapolis to Paris to escape from the notoriety. Here she soon met Lefevre, a man fully thirty years her senior, a married man at that, with two grown sons. Well, she fell passionately in love with him and became his mistress."

"How do you account for that odd choice?" exclaimed Smitty, rapidly puffing tiny clouds of smoke from a freshly lit cigarette.

"Well, I'll say that Katherine is impressed by brains. Now, if you will recall the reasoning in the recent Mystery of the Blue Bowknots, and if I add that Sprague was also a gallant father, you may find a clue. A parallel case in many ways, for Sprague, like old McMurtry, was also an attentive father. Far too much so," added Ford, becoming earnest and meditative.

"What do you mean?"

"Well, to be blunt, Sprague seduced his daughter when she was about twelve—infatuated with her," answered Ford unhurriedly. "It all occurred about two years after her mother ran away with their young chauffeur. The father and daughter were living in one of those square brick mansions built in the eighties. An older brother had been killed in the Argonne. So there they were, father and daughter living alone in an unnatural atmosphere of seclusion, seeking to avoid all the highly spiced talk caused by the elopement of Mrs. Sprague and later by the divorce which was spread all over the papers."

"How old did you say she was?" inquired Smitty incredulously.

"About twelve or thirteen but intellectually and physically precocious I would judge," replied Ford. "She must have been an attractive young thing just budding out into womanhood and quite a positive person for her age. Essentially father and daughter were pretty much the same type of mentality—two high-strung, intelligent people. Katherine has a mind like a man's and even at that age had a sort of adult appreciation of business. They were sympathetic to each other and thrust too much into each other's company at a time of great emotional stress . . ."

"What a calamity," said Smitty visibly affected. "Certainly a tragical background for the girl, wasn't it?"

"Bad from every angle—the mother running off with the chauffeur, only brother killed, violated by her father who became the subject of a front page murder."

"Terrible. You think this incident with her father fixated the girl's affections on older men?" asked Smitty.

"I am quite positive about that. Katherine's case is only one of several which have occurred in my practice, and each in a very different setting. Any District Attorney, whether in a big city or a peaceful rural county, can tell you that he must prosecute the offense of incest every now and then, and far more frequently than one would imagine. And the effect of such an incident on both parties is usually devastating. They have violated one of society's strongest taboos, and the sense of guilt grows and grows. The pressure of public censure is almost unbearable . . . ."

"I ask you again, why don't you follow your story, Benny. At eighteen, Katherine Sprague became Lefevre's mistress. Then what? She must have married to be Mrs. Foster. How about her marriage and divorce?"

"Well, it was like this," continued Ford. "About three years after her affair with Lefevre, she fell truly in love. It was with a young English Lord who apparently was crazy about her. Anyway, he wished to marry her, but made the grievous mistake of inviting her to the family's manor in Yorkshire to meet his parents. The chill of their reception more than rebuffed this highly sensitive, independent mid-Western girl. As members of an old English family, they had wanted to know more about their prospective daughter-in-law. They traced the scandal attached to her name through the sensational accounts of the murder of Howard Sprague. As it was, the mere suggestion of their son's marrying an American girl, even a rich girl like Katherine, had been an

affront to their British aristocratic pride. This additional
notoriety proved entirely too much. The thing was vetoed,
and the young Lord packed off without ado to his uncle,
British Consul in Teheran."

"And she bounced right back into the arms of French
journalism?" suggested Smitty.

"Not at all. Katherine herself does not lack pride, self-
reliance, or sensitivity. After this humiliation she felt uncertain and unsettled—and she temporarily lost her nerve.
She was convinced that life for her was finished. She wanted
to forget it all and attempted to extricate herself, so she fled
to the Riviera, that haven of forlorn ex-patriates from all
parts of the world. There she plunged into an orgy of indis-
cretions and promiscuity with a great variety of men. A few
of them were attractive but many were quite unprepossessing.
She said to me that she cannot understand what compelled
her to submit to men in whom she had no interest, who, at
times repelled her as individuals—men not necessarily with
breeding but to whom she attributed wisdom, assurance and
responsibility."

"How does your psychology account for that?" inquired
Smitty.

"Well, in such women a compulsion exists to make themselves wanted by many men. Many of her lovers wanted to
marry her but none seemed just the proper person for her.
After a few days or weeks with each, her interest would wane.
Then she met Henry Foster who fell ardently in love with
her."

"The man she married?" asked Smitty. "What sort of
fellow was he?"

"A man of thirty-five but already baldish. He shared her
own Hoosier memories and was an outstanding business
success, representing the Columbia Harvester Company in
all southern Europe. A man of experience and position

already wealthy through his own achievements. She wanted an unquestionable social status, so when he proposed marriage the third time she accepted him."

"And then *his* headaches began, I bet," interjected Smitty.

"Not exclusively. Her head also began to ache—very painfully in fact," continued Ford, chewing on the cigar which had gone out again. "Old memories began surging up and churning in her mind. She grew apathetic and taciturn. After a few months of wandering around Italy, Spain and Portugal, where Foster foolishly attempted to combine a wedding trip and his business interests, she was disillusioned. Her husband possessed few of the cardinal characteristics of her ideal, but she did not discover this until after marriage.

"They returned to the Midwest because of her lassitude. Foster had the mistaken idea that taking her back home to familiar scenes would cure her of her unhappy and distract moods. It was possibly the worst thing he could have done for her. Their arrival in Indianapolis was the signal for all the gossips to wag their sharp tongues about her folks' past, and about rumors they had heard of her escapades abroad."

"As you say, Benny, the pressure of public opinion is difficult to buck. Just goes to show how relative everything is," said Smitty. "The poor girl was simply born in the wrong place and at the wrong time. Had she been born back in Egypt and a daughter of the Pharaohs, her early incestuous relation would have received the blessing of the priests."

Ford chuckled. "If you continue to bask in my company much longer, my dear Watson," he said affably, "your cultural tolerance may lead you into disrepute with some of your colleagues up at St. James. Now, this time you quit interrupting, and I'll go on with the story. Katherine's husband brought half a dozen doctors into consultation. There were all sorts of diagnoses. You know how it goes in these baffling cases where nobody can say for certain whether the patient has a disease or a disease has got the patient; in other words, whether the condition is mental or really organic in origin. Finally, they decided she must have a brain tumor for which they operated but which they did not find. That's how she acquired the metal plate in her skull which you so ignominiously failed to observe."

"Really, Benny, at times you are a little trying. What has that to do with her and Lefevre?"

"Well, to begin again, the operating surgeon happened to be a college chum of Foster's and because of this friendship permitted him to stay at his wife's bedside while she was coming out of ether."

"Absolutely contrary to all good practice," exploded Smitty indignantly, and the blood mounted to swell the slightly tortuous arteries in his temples. "I have never permitted any relative to be present when a patient is coming out of ether—not even if that relative happened to be a doctor. No wife or husband should be around at such a time. They stay in the waiting room until the nurse calls them in."

"Agreed. Yours is the sound procedure," said Ford, "and this case proves it. Katherine afterward learned from her nurse what had happened, and assured me that she herself had no memory of it. While she was in that half-conscious state, sputtering and muttering and groaning as she came out of the ether, she betrayed some secrets of her past history, far too many of them, and then, to cap the climax, she suddenly raised her head and pointing a shaking finger at her husband, said in a quavering voice: 'Take that man away. I never loved him and I never will'."

"That was too bad," said Smitty soberly.

"Although Katherine's words were uttered in a semi-delirium," Ford went on, "they affected Foster profoundly. He left the hospital at once and returned home. There he broke open the only locked drawer in his wife's desk. It contained a small stack of old letters written by her young

English lord, and also—what was more important—recent letters from Lefevre in Paris, obviously written in reply to sentimental letters she had recently sent him. When Katherine had recovered from the operation sufficiently, Foster confronted her with these letters. She made no denials, nor did she protest any love for her husband. She felt she owed him no allegiance. So, only a little more than a year after their marriage, the Fosters were divorced. The people in Indiana agreed with one another in saying, 'It's her mother all over again!' "

"Really a bad egg?" asked Smitty.

"I don't think so. You see, she told me that she had become so disheartened and despondent with her headaches that she allowed herself to be operated upon although she felt way down deep that she had no brain tumor. She had heard it was a very serious operation and thought—even hoped—that she might die under it. It was a way out."

"That's a rare thing, if true," commented Smitty. "Sometimes my patients after an operation get into a state where they seem not to want to live. Don't think I ever knew a patient who submitted to the knife because he really hoped it would finish him."

"Perhaps not," assented Ford. "Anyway, Katherine Foster again lost her courage and confidence. She could not bear to stay where so much unsavory talk was again circulating about the Spragues."

"And this time your esteemed Dr. Watson has the right answer," said Smitty glibly; "she took the first French liner to Cherbourg—Lefevre waiting at the dock."

"Go to the head of the class, Smitty, your intelligence surprises me," bantered Ford.

"By the way, did you hypnotize this fair lady, too, Benny? I'm really not joshing now. Seems to me the revelations she made under ether were very much like the stuff the Stewart girl gave out under hypnosis."

"More, and astounding brilliance, my dear doctor," said Ford obsequiously. "Right again. Anything which diminishes the censoring part of the mind will allow all sorts of repressed thoughts to come out. Lots of drugs will do this—ether, alcohol in all its palatable forms, but especially as champagne, as your wide experience must have convinced you, Smitty. Recently we have been injecting a solution of sodium amytal into the veins of silent psychotic and other mental patients with the result that sometimes people who haven't spoken in months will talk volubly for about five minutes."

"I'll take champagne," laughed Smitty heartily. "Now back to the Spragues!"

"Well, when she was telling her story, she seemed to bear no resentment toward her father. I remember almost exactly her comment as she analyzed her father's character—'Sometimes I paint father as black, and he wasn't at all. Now I see he was just mixed up. I was afraid of father,' she said, 'but I loved him deeply.' Then I said to her, 'Perhaps you had to think of him severely to protect yourself from your own fond feelings toward him.' She chose not to reply to this but continued her own train of thought, almost in a soliloquy. 'Father was a man of strong will, the kind of man who knew what he wanted and who believed in going out and getting it. I remember the awful feeling of finality which crept over me when I looked in his face after he had died, and realized he could never again comfort me with that warm smile of his. I seemed to hear the soothing inflections of his voice when he would hug me and call me Baby Girl. He was proud of me and liked to show me off. But I know if he were here today even he could not comfort me now.'"

"Isn't that a different attitude from the ordinary?" queried Smitty.

"No, I should say it followed a rather common pattern. I also remember what Katherine, or maybe it was some other brainy girl-patient in a similar situation, said to me: 'There is nothing which father had done or left undone of which I can complain. No one is anything except that with which we endow him. Daddy was everything to me. He gave as much as he took—he opened a world to me—the world of ideas.' "

"I still would have expected that she'd hate him," said Smitty at the same time drawing from his pocket a fresh yellow pack of French cigarettes and indicating to the waiter a new round of drinks.

"On the contrary," replied Benny, "I can almost hear her say with a look of disdain—'I despised my mother and scorned her'—although it is apparent that unconsciously she followed her mother's pattern in her own affairs of love."

Smitty lit his cigarette and blew out a thin stream of smoke. He seemed to be reflecting on Katherine's plight and remarked irrelevantly, "You know, Benny, I keep on smoking these vile black things as long as I stay in Paris and like them. That's Paris."

"Love Paris, love her cigarettes," said Ford. "Unconsciously you're telling me almost what Katherine said about her father. You carry no aversion, no resentment toward these cigarettes which smell as bad as her father's reputation because they are a product of the Paris you love so well. Hatred and resentment against the father may be the conscious reaction in a case like Katherine's but an attachment and love for him would unconsciously influence the deeds and choices of a woman with an incestuous experience in a far wider range of behavior than one would suspect."

"And so you think that is the motive which impelled her to return to France and Lefevre?"

"Yes, I'm sure of it."

"It seems to me that you fellows always look at the sordid side. Why do you skip over the tough breaks, such as her father's disgrace, and the disappointments, such as the broken engagement with young Lord What's-his-name which may have left her no other choice."

"You may have something there, Smitty," agreed Ford, "but I am not certain that the marriage with the Britisher would have stuck either unless her psychological quirks were made conscious to her and she had come to relinquish the excessive yearning for fatherly men."

"You fellows are fettered by that psychic determinism— sounds rather fatalistic to me," protested Smitty.

"No, the psychological trends can be changed and if this does not occur completely, alternatives in life's patterns may become satisfactory. Take Katherine, for instance. From the calm, almost happy mien she seemed to show as she passed, I am inclined to think she may have done what was best for her, that is, for a while at least."

"Certainly she did not look unhappy," nodded Smitty. "You know, Benny, sometimes your stuff is really like Sherlock Holmes, it all seems so very apparent when explained."

Just then Claudette appeared in the doorway, came up to them with her gracious smile and sat down, unconcerned. Smitty ordered a cordial for her, then turned to Ford.

"Would you say, Benny, that some such motivation is back of these young women who hang around such places as this? I've had mighty little experience with them. Claudette, here, for instance. Not a bit coarse or brazen—almost modest—and taking care of Tubby. Yet she certainly has made up to an old codger like me. Thus far no hint of any offer of her professional services!"

Claudette looked up at him questioningly. She had heard her name although could not follow what was being said about her.

"Maybe she has made the mistake of sizing you up as a gentleman," chuckled Ford with an expansive smile at his friend, "and esteems politeness in a man."

"Which would account for her pointed lack of interest in you," countered Smitty with a twinkle. "But proceed with your profound philosophy and lore."

"Well, to go back to what you said a while ago about Katherine's having been born at the wrong time and place. Besides the Pharaohs and other instances of such practices and rituals which the anthropologists are hunting down just now, we have the infrequently mentioned example set for us by Lot's daughters."

"Never heard of them!" exclaimed Smitty. "Lot's wife, you mean, the lady who made herself famous by getting turned into a pillar of salt."

"Which event, so the Good Book states, gave the daughters an opportunity to ply her widower with inhibition-killing wine and then to consort with him," retorted Ford dryly.

"Hell, Benny, you do hunt up the damnedest stories."

"Book of Genesis. Might do you no harm to read the Bible once in a while instead of those worthless murder mysteries you always carry in your overcoat pocket. You see, the older and younger of Lot's daughters are both reported in the Good Book to have been with child by their father. But the escapade of Lot's daughters illustrates that it is not entirely the relative ease and laziness of their lives or any economic stress which makes one of these trim little girls a respectable seamstress and the other a sidewalk trotter. Nor is it lust alone that makes the youngsters from Copenhagen or Pekin studying at the Sorbonne, and the old married boys from Sleepy Eye, Minnesota, and New York, New York, keep the oldest profession flourishing in gay Paree; and equally, if less conspicuously, in our staid New England towns."

A familiar and bulky figure was walking rather hurriedly across the Place St. Michel towards the restaurant terrace.

"Ah!" exclaimed Claudette delightedly. She had been sitting the while politely uninterested. "Zere come ze Monsier Tooby. Now we have a good time."

X

THE GUN

As she showed the thin, round-shouldered, harassed-looking man into the waiting room, the self-effacing secretary had said, "Dr. Ford won't be a minute, Professor Langley". The Professor, who was often not too punctual in keeping his appointments had arrived at five minutes to nine. The hour of analysis was nine o'clock precisely—his customary time. Yet here it was already three minutes past nine and no sign of life on the other side of the door which led to the psycho-analyst's office . . .

The Professor in his impatience again took out his watch and looked at it intently for several moments. Then replacing it in his vest pocket he rose from his seat and went to the window which opened high up—sixteen stories above Gramercy Park. He stood there for what seemed a long time, looking down on the fine old sycamores which were bursting forth into the living green of spring leaves, the bushy shrubs and the grouped perennials of a darker green. He leaned out once, then drew back. The secretary had entered the room. She loitered, obviously rearranging the magazines on the low table while furtively casting a few anxious looks in the direction of the Professor. He turned and smiled at her reassuringly. "No," he said to her, "don't worry about me. I'm not thinking of taking a plunge out of the window! I was only admiring the scene and thinking how all that freshness of nature contrasted with my own dreary state of mind!"

The secretary said a few deprecatory words, polite and restrained and withdrew.

The Professor opened the high window and leaned from it. Then, drawing back, he said softly: "No, that's not the way out for me!"

He returned to a chair and listlessly handled the magazines on the table—an incongruous assortment for a doctor's office, he mused: The New Yorker, The American Scholar, The Saturday Evening Post, Peter Arno's cartoons, the Survey. It was an unusual thing, too, for a psychiatrist to select an office so high up. It seemed as if it was to challenge his clients: "Here you are—jump! Here's a way to be quickly finished with all your worries!" The Professor had once mentioned this to Dr. Ford who had replied with a chuckle: "Well, I've been here for fifteen years and no one has jumped yet! There are plenty of ways for people with a suicidal complex to do away with themselves—gas, poison, drugs, the subway tracks, the knife, the revolver, Professor." Then, after he had waited to note his patient's reaction, he added with a quizzical smile, "Such people have only to make their choice and this they almost invariably do according to their unconscious desires for passivity or violence!"

An unusual person, this Dr. Ford, thought the Professor, pleasant enough, not too formal, but inscrutable and detached. I have been seeing him for over a year, four times a week, and still I really know nothing about him personally, whether married, divorced, or has he any children! Even when he does loosen up he just talks more freely about me and hardly ever about himself. And that bland little secretary, usually invisible, is just a shadow of the doctor.

The Professor walked over to another chair and sat down —still thinking. A very capable psychoanalyst, Dr. Ford—or so he had heard, when he had first begun to fear for his reason and had made inquiries before seeking out this means of cure. Well, so far, the clever Dr. Ford had been of little use to him! This appointment today would be his last.

He would tell him so today and express his discontent with the results of this long series of treatments—almost nil. But he would ask the cryptic doctor before he ended the contact, just what he meant by that "choice". For clearly, in his own case, the Professor could think of only one way out. The high window did not even faintly tempt him. Out of the multitude of other ways there was only one for him, and he was going to use it soon. How long had he been coming here? A whole year! He had begun with such optimism! How many times had he lain uncomfortably on that couch in the doctor's office, endlessly reciting his dreams, letting all his painful inmost thoughts take form in words, withholding nothing . . . or almost nothing. A year! A year, at the end of which he had hoped at least to be able again to face his classes without terror. And here he was, at the end of that year just about where he had been at the beginning. Perhaps that was a euphemism, for at the start of treatment he had still had hope. Now that the analysis had done so little for him he had none; nothing to look forward to. He bit the cuticle about a fingernail, impatient with his own misgivings as to the cure.

The other night at dinner his wife, Lucy, had complimented him saying he looked "better". Well, that was just pampering him on her part, as were those friendly little dinners to which she had continued to invite him. Why did she persist in trying to patch up their wrecked marriage with good food and candlelight? Even the tact she used on those occasions was infuriating because it was so forced and obvious. She, the eternal complainer, trying to assume the role of the calm and capable wife catering to the helpless, neurotic professor-husband! Well, he'd show her! And also he'd show the doctor a thing or two . . . Maybe the doctor was not quite so imperturbable as he appeared.

The Professor nervously looked at his watch again. Only

five more minutes had passed—more waste of time! Still, what difference did it make when all this business of coming here for months had just been one gigantic waste of time and money, too, which he could really not afford.

The office door opened and Dr. Ford's calm, stolid face appeared. "Hello, Professor! I'm sorry I had to keep you waiting . . ."

"Not at all," replied the Professor meekly, suddenly weakening in his bold resolutions to confront the physician with his complaints. "I've had time to admire the view." As he entered the office and prepared to stretch out on the couch he gained courage to say in a bitter voice: "I was contrasting all that green freshness with the ashen gray of my mind. I even had a momentary impulse to plunge out the window—accept the lethal cure it offers. But then I decided that wasn't the way for me."

Doctor Ford took his seat at the head of the couch immediately without saying a word. Then, even though it was early morning he lit his customary cigar and when he saw that the patient was apparently relaxed, inquired:

"Things worse this morning, Professor?"

"What's happened to make things better?" the Professor retorted irritably. "You must admit, Doctor, that after working with me for more than a year, the results have been damned meagre. I told you I was afraid to begin analysis because if it didn't succeed, then I'd have nothing to look forward to. Well, the time has come to bring an end to all this futile probing. I don't mean to criticize you. You've tried your best, I suppose, but it just isn't in the cards. There's no solution. So, instead of droning away here on the couch I am about ready to take a long, endless nap."

"You didn't sleep well?" asked the doctor, intentionally ignoring the patient's threat.

"I spent a hell of a sleepless night, tossing and turning.

I'm feeling as low as a snake's belly this morning. Had a bad dream, woke up in a cold sweat, and couldn't get to sleep again."

"What was it?"

"Well, as near as I can remember, it ran something like this: I am sitting in my old tin Lizzy, the first car I ever owned, driving up a street. I turn to the right and find myself in a small, closed place like a park. I realize I have gotten into a blind alley from which there is no escape. In addition, I'm convinced I have committed a serious traffic violation. That fear is justified when I see a policeman approaching. He stands there bawling me out. He is just like the old, fat policeman of my boyhood—in the usual blue uniform, baggy trousers, helmet, club and all the rest. Then suddenly he turns out to be a woman, not a man! I awake in terror, the palms of my hands were ringing wet. Quite a concoction, wasn't it?"

"And what comes to your mind, Professor?" asked the doctor, repeating the analyst's formula.

The patient lay still for several minutes, then said:

"All sorts of impressions. Things flying round in my mind like the colors in a kaleidoscope. You cannot call them thoughts. But they are terrifying . . . Difficulties with my colleagues at the University . . . Students attacking me . . . Lawlessness . . . Revolt against authority . . . A turbulent scene 'round the guillotine during the French Revolution . . . The black nose of a cannon appears to protrude slowly through the aperture of the guillotine and the knife falls, cleaving the gun neatly. I can feel myself shuddering and—a bloody head rolls down the narrow, cobbled French street . . ."

Now the patient shuddered in actuality and pressed the back of his head deep into the leather couch pillow. His right hand began to tremble and he groaned and twisted his body as if in pain.

"What else, Professor? Let your mind drift," pursued the doctor, after a pause, noting his patient's agitation.

"Tough young ruffians driving me into a corner in a brick tenement yard," he continued, now speaking rapidly. "The same sort of things I've told you about so often, Doctor; the things that worry me. All the horrible thoughts that come to me when I lie sleepless at night. I don't have to dream that I am in a blind alley to know it—pushed by blind forces. I've been in a blind alley for a long time. No wonder it comes into my dreams—when I do manage to snatch a few hours of sleep."

"What else?" persisted the doctor.

"Oh, yes. I suppose the serious traffic violation is symbolic of my sins. Lord knows there's a long category. And I hate policemen. You remember the terrible fight I had with one only two weeks ago when he handed me a ticket for turning into a side street on a red light. For a moment I saw red. I burst forth that I was Professor Rollins Langley at the University. But it made no impression on him. I felt like smashing him in the jaw."

"But this policeman in the dream turned out to be a woman," Dr. Ford pointed out. "Perhaps you have always regarded all high authority as resting in a woman."

"Oh, I knew you'd say that, and call the guillotine affair a castration symbol. Of course I have memories of how my mother used to bully me and fill me with fear of the devil; my impotence to rebel which has galled me ever since I was a little boy and which intermittently made me feel weak and resentful at the world. This, in turn, again made me feel powerless. But all that has damn little to do with my insomnia. You wouldn't expect anyone to love his warden or jailer, no matter what the sex, would you?" snapped Professor Langley with increasing irascibility.

"May I say, nevertheless, that you seem extraordinarily aroused by the dreams and your associations," insisted Ford,

"I don't care, and it doesn't matter," retorted Langley peevishly. "I kept awake all night trying to find some solution to my problems. I just couldn't go back to my wife now, even if she'd have me. I couldn't stand that whining voice of hers. I just couldn't stand that reproachful look in her eyes every time I swear or come home smelling of liquor. And my intimate affairs with various other women! You know the pattern, Doctor: I begin well, then I waver, cannot go through with them and in the end collapse so dismally when I should stand up." He turned his head to look back at the doctor grinning like a naughty boy. "Women are all the same. They scare me when they come too close."

"Could it be, Professor, that maybe it is you who are unable to adapt yourself to any woman? But maybe we can change your attitude. Really, you have already changed a good deal, don't you think? You sometimes admit that you don't collapse and fail with the ladies so quickly or so often. And your wife has been trying to take care of you—by remote control, as it were—ever so patiently, since you separated five years ago. Your situation is really not too bad; now, is it?" continued Ford, pandering to the rebellious patient's plea for attention and sympathy.

"Maybe, but that isn't sufficient. That sort of thing doesn't help me—never did, and never will. My boy, Rollins, Junior, does not need me any more. The little I have will see him through college. And no one's life will be the less for the loss of mine. You know my work up at the University is so bad it's a wonder the students haven't registered a complaint with the Dean. Maybe they have. I'm sick of this hell of a world. No, I've decided to buy a pistol."

"Why just a pistol—there are so many other ways," said Ford calmly.

"There you go analytic again! Your whole approach is damned irritating and gets more so all the time. Of course I know I could slash my throat, or drink carbolic—ugh—or jump into the East River but that sort of thing is obnoxious to me. It horrifies me—this thing I'm about to do. But definitely I intend to shoot myself."

"You may recall, perhaps," said Dr. Ford with a little laugh, "that when Edward IV condemned the Duke of Clarence to death he generously offered him his choice as to the method. The intrepid Clarence chose to be drowned in a barrel of Malmsey—his favorite beverage!"

"Interesting and scholarly," sneered the Professor, "but like many of your anecdotes, it fails to intrigue me, especially this morning."

"Nevertheless," continued Ford, "some studies have been made on the choice of the method of suicide and its unconscious determination." Ford deliberately disregarded his patient's sober threat. "It's really not a matter of convenience —or even of fashion. I once had a patient, for instance, who, when he traveled to Europe, always took an inside cabin for fear he could not resist his impulse to go out through a porthole. However, his girth was such that this was actually quite impossible. When I asked him why it would not be simpler to throw himself overboard, he replied in astonishment that the thought had never even occurred to him."

"You fellows stick tenaciously to certain channels and work according to formula. I suppose you will ascribe some deep hidden meaning to his obsession about going through a porthole into the water—a rebirth fantasy, I suspect you would deduct in the case of the corpulent voyager," the Professor said sarcastically.

"Yes, that's right. And you have learned our analytic theories and have picked up the lingo entirely too glibly to benefit by them, Professor," said the doctor leaning forward and punctuating his words with a jabbing motion of his inevitable half-smoked cigar. He began speaking earnestly and positively. "It might have been exactly that. And I might also attach some symbolic significance to your predilection for the use of a gun," he added meaningly. Although the physician's voice remained calm, the look in his eyes betrayed some concern as to the seriousness of the patient's intentions. The patient heard only the voice but did not see the look—one of the advantages of the recumbent position for the patient and physician alike. Indeed, the Professor himself once remarked that he liked the arrangement, saying that it made him feel less conspicuous in his helplessness.

"Your interpretations no longer interest me, and your damned artificial serenity annoys me no end—sitting there in silent complacency as if you were thinking profoundly," objected the man on the couch. He took out his watch and consulted it. "My hour is nearly up. I'm tired of exposing my weaknesses and the mistakes of my life to you. With your permission, Doctor, I'll make you a present of the remaining time, give you a recess." He rose from the couch and stalked very deliberately out of the room with not a look behind him or a word of goodbye.

Doctor Ford sat motionless, his arms resting limply on the arms of the chair alongside the couch. His eyes followed the man as he disappeared through the door. Then he made an involuntary movement as if to stop him, or to follow him, but checked it and sat back. No, that was not the thing to do. The alternative to allowing the patient to leave was to force him to enter a mental hospital where the already hopeless man would be under lock and key and thereby possibly protected from himself. But the Doctor knew that Langley would never consent voluntarily to such a measure. The mere suggestion of the idea would imply that his condition had become desperate and this in turn would increase his feeling of failure and his drive towards self-destruction. The doctor shrugged. He would have to take the chance now as he had so often done before with other patients and accept, if need be, all the blame which the Professor's friends would heap upon him in the event of suicide. Anyway, the imminent likelihood of such an eventuality was slight. The Professor was intent on shooting and his threat to buy a gun revealed that he had none in his possession. In New York he would have a hard time to buy one without a permit. Dr. Ford rose and pressed a button knowing his secretary who rarely came during the day was there that morning.

"You may tell the next patient I'm ready," he said.

It was not the first time the Professor had made such threats; nor was it the first time he had left Dr. Ford's office so unceremoniously. But on this occasion he appeared more determined. As if in proof of this, the Professor turned his steps not toward home but eastward to Third Avenue, with its dingy, small stores and pawnshops. He would see what he could find there.

The first pawnbroker appeared virtuously shocked at the suggestion that he might sell a revolver to a customer without a permit. The second one was incensed and threatened to call the police but the third, after first refusing, followed his would-be customer to the door and offered to sell him a tarnished ring set with a small artificial pearl for only ten dollars. His beady eyes gleamed as he made the quite irrelevant offer.

"A veree wise purchase," he suggested slyly. "Veree wise, and cheap at the price."

The Professor understood the hint of bribery and after a moment's hesitation took the ring and paid for it. The pawnbroker left the ten dollar bill lying on the counter, as if he did not see it.

"Mister," he said, leaning close to the Professor, who became annoyed at the familiarity, and sinking his voice to a whisper, "I tell you vere you don't need no license for a gun. Down in Maryland you don't need no license to buy a gun. I tell you vere a frendt of mine vill sell you a gun—no, not a frendt of mine—but I know the place, I give you the address."

The old rascal proceeded to scrawl a name and a street number on a dirty piece of wrapping paper. "Gouldy," the pawnbroker said as he wrote the name. "Baltimore."

"How much will a gun cost me?" inquired the Professor.

"Fifty, maybe sixty dollars," said the pawnbroker. "I don't know. Vidout a license it costs awful dear . . ."

At Pennsylvania Station an hour later the Professor bought a ticket for Baltimore. Five hours after that, he entered a shabby pawnshop in a squalid Baltimore street. A few minutes later the shopkeeper and the customer were standing on the threshold of the shop, obviously quarreling. The pawnbroker was irate.

"Dot's not my bizness," he gesticulated angrily. "Some odder feller maybe—not me. Who vos it toldt you?"

Professor Langley thought it best not to reveal the source of his information and became silent as was his wont in the face of any attack and not only when a woman scolded him.

"Get out von my store. Get out quick."

Then Langley found himself again walking down the grimy street. It soon turned into a block of little white-stooped brick houses in front of which swarms of indolent negroes were lounging lazily in the first warm spring sun. He began to feel most desperately lonely and also very weary and dreary. This was just another of his botches. He wished that he had the gun at that very moment—he might have tottered up an alleyway and used it at once.

At eleven o'clock that night he had returned to his starting place. It had been such an unsuccessful and discouraging trip. The skin of his face had become more drawn than usual, and the muscles about his cheeks and all the way down to his throat were so taut that they actually hurt. After walk-

ing out of the somber, half-lighted Station which was filled
with a milling crowd of tired men and women in war-time
khaki uniforms, he quickened his pace and turned north on
Eighth Avenue with its dimmed lights. Reaching Thirty-
seventh Street he slowly moved east along the deserted
block, darkened by the shadows of tall loft buildings. From
the entrance halls of a few of them shone diffuse yellow
lights which relieved the gloom of the sidewalks. The street
was empty except for two dilapidated automobiles parked
on either side. He passed a prostitute who glanced an invitation to him as she slipped leisurely into the shadow of a
doorway. For a moment he was tempted but he automatically
kept going forward in his stride. Suddenly, from a dark door-
step a negro called to him:

"Hey, boss."

A black man in khaki uniform stealthily thrust his lithe
body from a doorway.

"Come ovah heah, Mister," he whispered. "Youh wanta
buy some cigarettes—I got plenty of 'em heah—Camels."

He showed a half-open, worn brown canvas bag from
which the square ends of several cartons protruded. The
abrupt intrusion of the negro's words into his dismal musings
had startled the Professor but relieved his feeling of loneliness for a moment.

"I don't care to buy any cigarettes," said the Professor becoming formal and wary.

"Mister, how much does they pay foh 'em heah in New
York?" asked the soldier.

"I don't know—twenty cents a pack, maybe."

"Dat all?"

"Well, I guess so," said Langley longing to edge away as
usual when he felt he could not cope with a situation.

"I'll sell youh a carton foh two-fifty," said the negro looking straight at him, "and white man, youh bettah buy 'em,"
he added with an intimidating threat in his voice.

"But I don't really want them," replied Langley hesitatingly, and he became conscious of the wetness of his palms.

"You cain't git Camels nowheres dese times," insisted the black man moving uncomfortably closer to him so that their faces almost touched.

"I'll take a carton," faltered the Professor and gave the man three dollars which he promptly pocketed. Langley felt like blubbering at this new instance of his cowardice, and the old idea about shooting himself recurred involuntarily to his mind. It kept him fixed to the spot when of all things he wished most to tuck the cigarettes under his arm and slink away.

Reluctantly renewing the contact with the negro who had just humbled him Langley said, "I want to buy a gun. Do you know where I can buy a gun?"

The negro's eyes widened so that they terrified him.

"What foh youh want to buy a gun, boss," he asked, becoming interested. His intonation was conversational, confidential, almost familiar—all of which did not tend to reassure the Professor, but he mustered enough courage to say in his somber voice:

"I want to shoot myself."

"Man, why foh youh wants to shoot youself?" exclaimed the negro.

"Oh, life just is not worth living." It was the old, familiar complaint which he had so often made to Doctor Ford.

"I kin git a gun foh youh but it cost youh plenty o' money," the negro said, "I can git 'em from de Army. If a feller loses his gun in de Army it costs him thirty dollars so if I git you a gun it'll cost youh fifty dollars."

"Would it be a good gun?" asked Langley incredulously.

"Sho, Army gun. But, man, why foh youh wants to shoot youhself. Shoot de odder man—dat's what I does. I ben ovah dere in Africa."

"No, I must shoot myself," said Langley, at the same time

despising himself for his candor with the ignorant stranger
and his own cringing. He could feel the familiar resentment
at his own subservience creeping into his mind, revealing
itself in his voice and in his legs which wobbled like jelly.

"Don' do dat, man," protested the negro with gleaming
eyes, "why don' youh go down New Orleens."

"And why should I want to do that?" inquired Langley
wondering what might come next.

"Youh wouldn't need no gun dere. Down New Orleens
youh kin drown youhself in a barrel of molasses."

"And why do you say that," asked the Professor entirely
baffled by this apparently irrelevant suggestion.

"Because den youh sho would die a sweet death," said the
negro with shrill, high-pitched laughter and clapping his
hands on his thighs.

The Professor was nettled. The negro's cheap ridicule
irritated him. Somehow it reminded him of the doctor's
reference to the Duke of Clarence's death in a barrel of
wine. The doctor, too, never seemed to take him seriously
enough. The negro's logic sounded like the doctor's. He had
often repressed his resentment of the doctor just as he now
found himself doing with the disrespectful black man. He
was a damned insolent fellow but Langley feared to arouse
his anger, so he merely repeated quietly:

"I told you I want to buy a gun."

"Look heah, Mister," exclaimed the black man, "I kin git
youh a gun if youh pays me fifty dollars. But why don't
youh give me de gun and I'll shoot youh sho—den youh'll be
all dead and I'll have de gun and de money, too."

"Oh, I'm afraid that would not do," stammered Langley
glumly.

"Sho, I'll shoot youh dead alright," the soldier went on
reassuringly.

"You might get into trouble with the law."

"Don't youh worry 'bout me—youh won't have to. I'll

shoot youh so quick youh nevah would know it. But man, youh ain't worry 'bout me beint cotched. Youh jes' don' want me to shoot youh—wants to do it youhself—youh suttinly is a sore head."

This last again sounded to Langley disconcertingly like Ford's interpretation of the idea of suicide as being a primary hostility against his mother and wife which he had turned against himself.

"No," he said unconvincingly, "I wouldn't want anything to happen to you," and he seemed to himself like a pouting little boy.

"Dey wouldn't cotch me. Beside dat I loves to shoot white men. I shoot lots of dem ovah dere in Italy. I don't like how dey treats us colored people ovah heah. I comes fum Philly. I don't like de way de Army treats me—like dose cotton field niggers fum Alabama. Don't be so mean, man, lemme do it," he pleaded.

"No, I have got to shoot myself," reiterated Langley lugubriously. His voice sounded inane and empty, and he felt perspiration running from his hands in drops.

"I heered you say dat befoh, but what good dat gun to youh after youh dead. Jes' give it to me after you buy it an', Mister, please say I kin shoot youh."

The Professor sensed the logic of the plea but answered obstinately, "that won't do".

"Look heah, boss, foh fifty dollars I kin kill youh an' don' need no gun, jes' like dis way," and the negro spread his powerful-looking, long-fingered hands as if to clasp them about the Professor's trembling throat. He moved menacingly closer and hissed with released ferocity. "I'se tired messing 'round with youh. Youh bulls too much. If youh want to die, die any ole way or hush up."

In the negro's ruthless insistence there was something brutal which reminded the Professor of the analysis which always got back to him and his evasions. Now the black man said, "Maybe ef youh gits too sore head I'll jes' kill youh' 'cause youh is white." Langley felt his heart pounding against the chest wall and a clammy, cold sweat covering his body.

Then the negro seemed to reflect that this approach would be financially profitless and he became conciliating and ingratiating again. The Professor breathed easier.

"I'll tell youh, boss, ef youh jes' won't give me de gun, I'll git de gun foh youh. Meet me right heah tomorroh night 'bout dis time. I'll have de gun an' youh have de dough. Maybe youh'll let me shoot youh anyhow. Youh ain't ornery as all dat—is youh—long as youh goin' to die."

Just then a police car entered the dark street from the east. It stopped a hundred feet away and one of the officers got out to inspect a door. The soldier cut short his words and darted deeper into a shadowy recess. Langley hastily retreated toward Eighth Avenue. He felt a sense of relief as he turned the corner and almost ran toward Thirty-fourth Street which by contrast seemed brilliant and safe in the dimmed lights of the black-out. He dipped into the entrance of the subway, scurried down the steep flight of the stairway and rushed to catch a northbound train just roaring into the station. As he sank, still trembling, into a seat of the brilliantly lighted car, the grind and roar of the train sang a soothing lullaby of security for him.

Doctor Ford was relieved when he peered into the waiting room the next morning at nine and saw Professor Langley reclining in an arm-chair quietly fingering a magazine and smoking a cigarette. His strained look had vanished. He rose, entered the office with a cheery good-morning, and at once took his place on the couch.

"I had a most unusual and interesting experience last night, Doctor," said the Professor without waiting for the doctor's usual "what's on your mind today". "A negro soldier offered to deliver a gun to me tonight. He turned out to be quite a psychologist."

"Well, many untutored persons, like old Irishwomen and Negro mammies, are at times. They resemble young children —often see the truth—the naked truth—and blurt it out without the fear of those consequences which makes us civilized folk cautiously suppress our feeling and opinions. What did your colored friend say to you?"

"He exposed some of my weaknesses, all right, and corroborated some of those pet theories of yours about my selfishness and self-love and bitterness against the world. Perhaps what he said impressed me so much and at that moment because you had prepared me for it in so many and varied ways. Maybe it was the simple, elemental and forceful way in which the soldier expressed it. But I don't think I'll keep the appointment with him tonight."

The Professor's face relaxed into a sheepish, boyish grin as he said with a little laugh, "I guess I'm cured, at least of the idea that I must take the lethal way out of my problems."

XI

CHRISTMAS CARD

It was a few days before Christmas. More than three years had passed since the Japanese had made their wanton descent on Pearl Harbor and the people's minds had burned with indignation but were sobered by the realization that they had been forced into the murderous misery of war. In Dr. Ford's morning mail, along with the drug firms' expensive, lurid advertisements of the latest panacea, vitamins, the usual personal and professional letters, and a couple of bulky periodicals, was an early batch of Christmas greeting cards. One of them caused the doctor to tilt back his chair, close his eyes and smile in quiet reminiscence and appreciation. On it a child had drawn in green crayon a Christmas tree and under it the crude picture of a little boy with golden yellow hair, wearing red pants and a bright blue shirt. Under it the child had painstakingly printed the inscription:

DOCTOR FORD MERRY XMAS
HIS FREND, PERRY BROWN.

Dr. Ford kept the card on his desk in full view all that day. It was the twenty-sixth hand made card that he had received in as many consecutive years on which the name of Perry appeared. Each one of them had kept fresh in his mind one of those happy experiences which come now and then to every physician and serve to lighten the recurrent disappointments in his struggles with the physical and mental illnesses of man, some of which he knows from the start must end in defeat for him or at the best in an unsatisfactory compromise.

The card stayed there the next day. It set him to musing and as he rose heavily from his chair that evening after

206

work he drew from his history files on the top shelf of a closet a dust covered, fading pasteboard box labeled 1919. The year had meant much to him—a year of hope for permanent peace in the world and the advance of brotherhood of man. These had been the aim of "the war to end all wars —to make the world safe for democracy". Bah! The new World War had smashed all these promises of 1919 and all the havoc and sacrifices of four years of the first war appeared futile. As he thought it over, he suddenly felt tired and disheartened.

Turning to his file of patients' histories he found under the name of Perry a sheaf of notes in his own hand—quite unintelligible to anyone but himself. Attached to them was a typewritten letter dated Binghamton, New York, December 5th, 1919.

"My dear Dr. Ford:

You probably will not recall me as one of your students of the class of 1914 at the Medical School but, as you see, I do remember you and am writing to seek your help in a case which puzzles me. The patient is a Mrs. Perry, about thirty-five, living in a village near here. She has been bed-ridden for almost four years and says she cannot walk. All sorts of diagnoses have been made by good local men and by specialists from Rochester and Syracuse. She reminds me of that man with 'sciatica' who fooled all of us students so badly but who you showed was really affected with an hysterical symptom.

Do you think you could come up to see her over some weekend? I know I am asking a great deal of you as the fee will be minimal but there will be scientific compensations, I feel sure, and my wife and I will try to make your stay at our home comfortable.

Yours sincerely,

Thomas Sawtell, M.D."

A blurred carbon copy of Ford's reply had been filed with the history:

> *"December 9, 1919*
>
> *My dear Dr. Sawtell:*
>   *Let me acknowledge your letter of recent date. I remember you and your side-kick, Kaufman, well—two men who always kept me on my toes with unanswerable questions. But it gratifies me particularly that you should remember me. I shall be very happy to come up to Binghamton over the last weekend of December and look forward to an interesting visit.*
>
> > *Yours sincerely,*
> > *Benjamin Ford."*

A heavy storm covered the mountainside of the Poconos with a glistening white blanket as the Lackawanna express sped over the many-curved tracks from New York City toward Binghamton. Late on a Friday evening when Ford arrived, Sawtell was waiting for him on the snowy platform of the old-fashioned station. He barely recognized the changed figure which came toward him with an extended hand. Sawtell, now in his early thirties, had become a ruddy-cheeked man, the slimness of youth already giving way to a premature chunky stoutness of approaching middle age. His face was almost hidden by the up-turned collar of a raccoon coat with its fur tinged yellow by time and exposure.

"Well, it certainly is good of you to come, Dr. Ford. We'll start right for my house. Gert is expecting us. No, of course we are putting you up. Let's go. With the freeze which has set in, chains don't help much but I'll try to keep the old tin Lizzy from spinning off the road."

On the trip from the station the two men spoke seldom and briefly. Sawtell gave his full attention to keeping the light car from skidding into the high frozen snow banks. After ten minutes the car came to a slow, sliding stop. Sawtell shifted into low gear and turned cautiously into a narrow, ice-coated alley-way which ended at a frame garage at the side of the house. They got out and Sawtell leading they picked their way to the back door which opened into the kitchen. A pleasant-looking, cheery, quick-moving young woman had just put the percolator on an electric stove. She looked up with a hearty smile of welcome and exclaimed:

"Why Salty, you ought to be ashamed of yourself—bringing Dr. Ford in through the kitchen—and take off your galoshes outside. I have already started perking the coffee for I knew you'd be frozen. How do you do, Dr. Ford?"

"Of course you realize by now that you are meeting the wife, Dr. Ford," said Sawtell. "Gert, how's the kid?"

"Oh, Peppy's been tight asleep for hours. Peppy is what we call Thomas Sawtell, Jr., Dr. Ford. That's to distinguish him from Salty. Did you know that they called him Salty in college?"

"No, I must say I didn't but I can imagine why he got the name."

"Now, if you men will just go into the office—it's the warmest place in the house—I'll be in with the coffee in a few minutes. You'll find some snacks there."

The small extension young Dr. Sawtell used as his office had been added to the old house which had become vacant through the death of an uncle just after he returned home from his internship. It was a good-sized room with a direct connection to the house through a narrow passageway. An old-fashioned, mahogany roller-top desk, which Sawtell said he had found in the library of the house, was the most prominent piece of furniture. Between two windows looking out upon the frozen alley-way stood a table on which Mrs. Sawtell had placed a platter of carefully cut sandwiches and a dish of walnuts.

"Have a chair", said Sawtell as he beamed at the sandwiches. "Great girl, Gert. You know, Dr. Ford, we were engaged all the time I was in medical school. We married just as soon as I finished my internship and everything has been just fine since."

Mrs. Sawtell came in carrying a tray with a coffee set which she put beside the sandwiches on the table. "Perhaps you'd prefer a highball, Dr. Ford. Salty will take care of that—his medicine chest always has plenty of spiritus frumenti. I'll leave you two men together. I know he will want to tell you all about that Mrs. Perry. Salty's all wrapped up in his discovery—it's a good thing I'm not a jealous doctor's wife. And now good-night."

"Great girl, Gert", repeated Sawtell enthusiastically. "Great doctor's wife and a wonderful mother—does everything so calmly that difficult things seem easy. I've done all right up here and it's due a lot to Gert. No telephone mix-ups or lost calls when she's around."

"It comes as something of a relief to me to sense the feeling of understanding and contentment in your home," said Ford. "You know, in my practice I see so much of the other side of the marriage adventure, people who bicker and disagree until either the husband or wife, or both of them, gets sick over it. It's grand to see the happiness so apparent here. You know, I am only now beginning to remember you as you were in college, Dr. Sawtell, or may I call you Salty?"

"By all means. You know, Dr. Ford, I've had great luck ever since I started. The best man in town, Dr. Powell, who was getting along in years, asked me to take his night calls. Then during the third year I had his practice while he was down with a stubborn attack of flu. I think he liked the way I refused to take some patients who wanted to switch from him. There always are patients who want to adopt the new doctor. Anyway, I am his regular assistant now, besides a nice little practice of my own. This Mrs. Perry is one of my own cases although pretty near every other doctor in town has seen her since she took to bed."

"What became of your old chum, Kaufman?" asked Ford. "I always think of you two men together. I'll bet that you young rascals sat up nights thinking up questions to stump the instructors."

"Oh, only once in a while when we needed a little relaxation," laughed Sawtell and a wide, boyish grin lighted up his face. "Kaufman is down in Newark specializing in stomach work—doing darn well, too. He came through here last fall with his wife on their way to the Syracuse game—he is a Colgate grad. We had quite a bull session. By the way, he mentioned you and that lanky Yankee partner of yours who also used to talk to the students about psychoanalysis and Freud. You know, we fellows didn't fall for that stuff much but Kauf always claimed that even though it sounded dippy, there seemed to be something in it. Psychiatry certainly got a boost with the army in France."

"Yes, and what did Kauf have to say?"

"He said he is discovering more and more that the mind has a god-awful influence on the stomach. Told a funny little story. He had a patient who complained of stomach trouble all the time. Kauf couldn't find anything wrong—all the tests and x-rays negative. So finally Kauf told him it was nervousness. The patient replied, 'Well, Doctor, you aren't the first one who made that diagnosis. The night orderly in the hospital where I had my appendix out for chronic indigestion and pain made it, too. I guess the surgeon didn't know what else to do so he cut me up. After the operation I would lie there nights groaning and grunting and complaining to the old-time orderly with whom I had become quite chummy. One night he said to me, look here, Mr. Meyerberg (that was the patient's name), the trouble with you ain't your guts, it's that you ain't got any'."

"That's a good one," laughed Ford. "It's been my observation that in times of peace the stomach seems to be the organ most often upset by worry but with the soldiers in the recent war it was the heart. Now somebody's got a new high-sounding name for it—neurocirculatory asthenia. Cold feet is what the boys used to call it when a kid was afraid to fight. Sometimes they'd say he was scared stiff. We psychiatrists call this last reaction a functional paralysis. Sounds very important, doesn't it?"

"Which brings us to Mrs. Perry," added Sawtell. "Now there's a family which never seems to be out of trouble. Three days ago her little girl, Julia, broke her femur when she tumbled while sliding down hill. I was called and as she needed a pulley and traction for the fracture I had to bring her down to the hospital here in town. Her mother, as I wrote you, has been bed-ridden for three years. Her father runs a small general store in Hesta—just a village—and is having a bad time of it. Nearly everybody up there has a car now—a Ford or Overland or something—and they come to town to go to the movies and shop at the Five and Ten, or the A and P or Sears. It's been hard on Perry. He slaves twelve hours a day—is very accommodating—too much so with some of the deadbeats who never pay anybody including their faithful doctor, yours truly. But it looks to me as though Perry is playing a losing game."

"How old is Perry?"

"My guess would be Luther Perry is about forty—a little man, getting bald in front, too many wrinkles in his face. He's worried to death at home and in business. He has managed to carry on although he has only one clerk to help him where he used to have two."

"And Mrs. Perry, how old is she?"

"Oh, I should say thirty-five. The Perrys are local people—plenty of them on both sides of the river between here and Owego. Mrs. Perry is of Bohunk stock—came from down Wilkes-Barre way. I don't know where she met Perry. Some folks say she is half Jewish—or her mother was. She used to be a darn good-looking woman and still shows signs of it.

Won't you have a high ball, Dr. Ford. I have some excellent Teachers Scotch. Somehow I have clung to Teachers since my college days at Princeton. My folks come from these parts. There were a number of teachers among them. They were Presbyterians and frowned on whisky though they did not actually forbid my drinking. In college I was intrigued to discover that a 'Teachers' whisky existed—somehow it appeared to me to be less of an offense to drink from a bottle labeled 'Teachers'."

"And so you may offer it to a former teacher without the risk of reproach," said Ford smiling. "I'll join you—a long drink, please."

"That reminds me of one of my patients," resumed Ford after Sawtell had returned with the drinks from the laboratory which opened off the far end of the office. "She told me that when she was a little girl her over-solicitous mother used to dose her plentifully every winter with Scott's Cod-liver Oil Emulsion and stuck to plain castor oil in days when most children were getting syrup of figs. All her stomach aches were attributed to candy, and sweets were taboo for her. All the bad tasting things which came from the drug store, however, were good for one. Her heart jumped for joy when she found that the corner drug store also sold candy. She seemed less guilty even as an adult if she bought candy at a pharmacy. But let's get back to the Perrys—you wrote me that Mrs. Perry cannot walk."

"That's right, she has not left her bed for these three years—her legs crumple under her—besides she has many other complaints—there is a loss of appetite and refusal of food. She has lost nearly forty pounds. There have been times when she cannot keep anything on her stomach for days. All sorts of doctors—osteopaths—homeopaths and regulars—all sorts of diagnoses but the one which has seemed to stick longest and to be most acceptable to everyone is 'fallen stomach and intestines'. She's a mystery—a hospital

ward all in herself. There is no doubt that she is suffering
intensely mentally as well as physically. I have watched her
at times when she looks extremely hopeless and depressed—
as though she had lost her last friend. And I guess she has.
Neighbors have long since gotten tired of pitying her and
running in to help with the housework for a few hours. Her
little girl, Julia, the one now in the hospital with the broken
leg, has done much of the work about the sick-room—fetch-
ing and carrying at her mother's direction from the bed—
being rewarded by kissing and petting and endearments.
She has become a somber little creature, a pale and spindle-
legged child from being housed-in too much."

Having recited this report, Salty felt entitled to a reward
from Teachers and proceeded to freshen up his high ball.

"Is Julia the only child?" asked Ford.

"Yes. As I remember it she had two other children—boys—
each of whom died shortly after birth. Anyway, Julia has
been an only child whom her mother has bound very closely
to herself and Julia is over-attached to her mother through
fear and pity."

"You said Mrs. Perry has mental symptoms—depression—
anything more?" asked Ford crushing a couple of walnuts
in his hand.

"Yes, there have been disturbing dreams which awaken
her at night in cold sweats. The sweats made one doctor think
her case might be tuberculosis—but her sputum and everything is negative, including x-rays, and she has no fever."

"What does she dream about?"

"Now, Dr. Ford, how should I know. I'm not a psychiatrist and that dream stuff in psychoanalysis is the hardest
thing to swallow in the whole business."

"Maybe she'll tell us her dreams if we don't press her too
hard," suggested Ford.

"Don't include me. All I'm going to do is introduce you
and vanish."

The 'phone rang. Sawtell glanced at the clock. "Eleven. Her usual time," he said. "I'll bet that's she now." He took up the receiver.

"Yes, Mrs. Perry—he came this evening. Well, try to settle down. You've nothing to fear. Better take ten grains of trional—that should give you some sleep . . . I can't say just when. Probably not until around noon . . . Yes. We'll surely be there tomorrow. Good-night."

"Is there anything more you wish to tell me, Salty? I imagine you'll want to turn in after a hard day's work."

"Yes, I have been on the go since eight this morning, with a call to a pneumonia at three last night. And tomorrow there are at least five calls I should make before we set out for Hesta. It's six miles from here and the going will be none too easy with the frozen roads but I'll call back here for you at noon. Sleep as late as you like. A smart high school girl comes in on Saturdays to help Gert about the house and there'll be breakfast for you when you want it. Have another little nightcap and we'll stumble up to your room."

The Perry house stood like a small box on top of a steep little knoll just off the intersection of three roads which formed a Y around which were clustered a few small stores, among which Perry's was the largest. Sawtell drove past the store, his chains clanking and grinding the ice-crust. He veered sharply off the highway and sped swaying up the hill on an icy road sprinkled here and there with ashes. Miss Abbie Perry, the sick woman's sister-in-law, a stout, sour-faced woman of fifty, opened the door.

"Miss Abbie," said Sawtell, "this is Dr. Ford, I've told you about him. He has come up all the way from New York to see Edna. How has she been?"

Miss Abbie nodded and stared challengingly at Dr. Ford. "She hain't bin tew well. Said she ha'ent slept much. How's little Julia, Doctor?" she asked eagerly, more interested in the child than her mother.

"Oh, she'll be all right but it'll take time—six weeks. Misses her mamma and I guess her mother would miss her even more if you hadn't come over to help, Miss Abbie. Can we go up now?"

"No need tew hurry so—but ef you want tew—guess she heerd you come up the hill."

The physicians ascended a steep flight of stairs which led from the front sitting room to the floor above. The door of the room in which Mrs. Perry lay faced the narrow landing at the head of the stairs. The room's width covered the entire front of the house—about twenty feet—but it was shallow—not more than ten feet in depth. The wide double bed stood at the left of the door and almost touched the opposite wall where two windows faced toward the southwest. They looked out upon snow covered wooded hills beyond the roofs of the houses along the fork of the roads. A brilliant sun had forced its way through the mist of the valley and flooded the room with a dazzling light reflected from the whiteness of the earth. On a white painted dresser, covered by a coarse yellow linen runner, lay a set of imitation ivory toilet articles. The yellowish white back of the brush contrasted with the whiteness of the handle of the button hook and shoe horn. The set must have been accumulated piece by piece over a dozen years. No garments were visible. "A sickroom—not a bedroom"—noted Ford to himself. Both the room and bed were neat and clean. Whatever antipathy Miss Abbie may have felt toward her sick sister-in-law did not affect her pride in her own reputation for tidiness.

"This is Dr. Ford whom I brought to see you, Edna," said Sawtell.

The wan, resigned looking woman smiled feebly but

sweetly with her gentle eyes. "I'm glad you've come", she said, putting out a thin hand. "I'm very weary and the months pass slowly. Dr. Sawtell told me that you might help me—maybe to walk again." She began weeping but soon regained control. "I mustn't," she said.

"Suppose you let me see those cantankerous legs that haven't worked for you for so long," said Ford.

He drew out first one leg, then the other from underneath the bedclothes. Both were limp and thin but the thinness was symmetrical. The legs were clean as though the patient had been cared for by a professional nurse. Ford said a word of praise about her neatness.

"You know, Doctor, I have learned to take a complete sponge bath in bed without spilling a drop of water," she said with a gleam of pride in her face and voice.

"That is a feat," agreed Ford as he tapped the knees and ankles with a little triangular rubber hammer and then stroked the soles of the feet with a pin and determined that the reflexes were normal. He cast a glance at Sawtell who stood watching which said plainly to him, "Your diagnosis has been correct". Then he reflected, "No real loss of power exists in these legs. She merely has lost the desire and ability to use the power which exists."

Aunt Abbie had mounted the stairs with a light step unexpected in so stout a woman and eyed the whole scene with disapproval.

"I'm going to leave you alone with Dr. Ford, now, Edna. I'll drop by at the store and tell Luther to get somebody to drive the doctor back to my house when he is ready to go. How long do you think it will be, Dr. Ford?"

"I can't tell. But I'll get back somehow," said Ford.

The doctor drew up a chair alongside the bed so that he did not face his patient. The conversation began casually about the bad roads, the Susquehanna, its rifts and floods and big bends, the differences between size and flow in New York State and Pennsylvania where Mrs. Perry had come from. And gradually Mrs. Perry began to talk, telling in detail of her physical symptoms and her earlier life in Kingston across the river from Wilkes-Barre. There after graduation from high school at eighteen—"the first in her class"—she had met Luther Perry, then working in a department store and had married him soon after. Two baby boys born within the first three years had died in infancy. Then she had not desired more children and Julia had been accidental.

"Were you in love with Luther when you married?"

"Oh, I don't know. I can't say that I was or that I wasn't," she replied objectively. "Mother was strongly in favor of it. The Perrys are a good family up this way. That always meant a lot to mother but I guess, too, I wanted to get away from home," she sighed and paused.

After several minutes she resumed her narrative and under gentle encouragement by the physician she told more intimate things—her mother's mother had been a Jewess, married to a Czech storekeeper named Capek and a Protestant. Her own mother had married a local boy, Jim Walters, son of an owner of a small coal mine to which he fell heir. Her mother's brother had been away at Norristown in an insane asylum for years.

"Tell me a little more about that, won't you? What did your uncle suffer from?" inquired the doctor.

"I don't know—it was all very vague. Uncle Lawrence was one of those family skeletons that one rarely talks about and never displays."

"Did you know him?"

"No, not really, but I remember dimly that when I was a little girl of five mother took me with her when she went down to see him—I think she left me in a room outside the ward. But I have always carried with me an impression of gloom and mystery and secrecy and disgrace about that asylum and Uncle Lawrence being there."

"Were your parents happy together?" asked Dr. Ford intentionally changing the topic.

Mrs. Perry shook her head and explained that her father had lacked the ability to run the mine, could not stand his failure and quarreled often with her mother. At such times he taunted her about her "Jew-blood". The patient, too, had acquired a sensitivity about the remote Jewish heritage of which few of her friends knew and it had made her uncertain of her social position. At length Mrs. Perry started weeping anew.

"Oh, Doctor, I don't like to give in to whatever it is. It makes me feel miserable to be so helpless and useless, flat on my back. I'm a wreck but I can't help it and don't want it. I know I'm too grown up to be babied this way—my will seems paralyzed as well as my legs—I always seem to do the wrong thing—I'm such a mill-stone about Luther's neck."

"Is Luther good to you?" asked Ford.

"Sometimes I think he's far too good," she looked dejected and became quiet for a time.

Ford glanced at his watch—over two and a half hours had passed since Mrs. Perry first began telling her story. "I think I may be tiring you a little," said he. "Perhaps we'd better rest a while. Suppose I take a walk and then come back. But first I'll ask Miss Abbie to bring you some tea and crackers."

He started up the country road which led through the sloping, white fields back of the house, breathing deeply in relief from the long confinement in the sickroom. The sun had warmed the air and softened the crusts of ice. As he walked he began to think over the facts he had learned, searching for the secondary gain which comes to a patient through most hysterical symptoms although this gain is achieved so indirectly and at so great a cost in suffering. The paralysis allowed her to evade society—that much was evident—but the strictly social reasons mentioned by the sufferer for her insecurity with the other women of the town seemed insufficient to account for such severe self-punishment. The attachment to her little girl which had the double function of enslaving the child as well as over-indulging her could not be neglected as a possible motive for the withdrawal. But Mrs. Perry's very long silence after her reply about the kindness of her husband—for whom she professed no great affection—seemed significant. Ford's mind reverted to her phrase, "far too good", and he pondered for a long time over its implication.

It was three o'clock when Ford returned to the Perry house refreshed by his tramp in the wintry air. A neighbor was visiting with Miss Abbie in the kitchen. They had evidently been discussing him because as he passed by he heard her say:

"All I heerd him do war nothing. If thet's what they call a great New York specialist, excoóse me." The wry expression of the spinster's face did not change as she poked her head out of the kitchen door and remarked to him, "Gettin' warmer out?"

Mrs. Perry had taken the tea and crackers. Her eyes were red with crying but she gave Ford a look of friendliness as he resumed his seat in the chair at the head of the bed. The story continued as before—little additions, little corrections, but with new accents and then an observation made for the first time.

"You know, sometimes at night I wake up wringing wet—all exhausted from ghastly nightmares."

"In terror?" asked Ford with sympathetic interest.

"Oh, Doctor, I must tell you," she cried, leaning toward him and grasping his arm with a trembling hand and forearm. "I've never told anybody before. I see such frightful things—I can't stand it, cross-bones, cross-bones, always cross-bones. At night they come out of the walls in white; during the day they are black—they pop out of the wall—tiny cross-bones, long, very thin cross-bones. They keep on coming and coming at me when I don't want them—when I don't expect them. Oh, they frighten me so," she sobbed and kept on sobbing.

"You need not fear them so, Mrs. Perry," said Ford reassuringly.

"Oh, Doctor, that's not all—in the heads of the bones are eyes which leer at me and mock me. White slimy eyes in the black bones and horrible black-green eyes—burning snakes' eyes in white bones and thousands of squirming snakes—oh, they frighten me so—they are so terrifying. I'm too scared to go to sleep at night."

"Why didn't you ever tell anybody about this before?"

"I was afraid to. I thought they would say that I was crazy and would send me away—like Uncle Lawrence in Norristown. Oh, I'm not crazy, am I, Doctor? Tell me I'm not crazy," she pleaded with tears streaming down her cheeks.

"No, you're not going insane, Mrs. Perry. Our minds play queer tricks on us sometimes. Yours has on you."

She fell back deep into her pillow in the relaxation of exhaustion. Ford noticed the bedclothes at the foot of the bed move as the patient unconsciously turned her feet in and out several times. Then she spontaneously exclaimed:

"It's the horrible things you have to keep to yourself. If your house burns down everybody knows it and they are sympathetic. You can't let them see what burns inside of you."

"Perhaps it may be possible to relieve these concealed fires which scar and sear you—perhaps it may be better to expose them and allow them to flare up momentarily and thus burn out rather than have them smoulder and scorch. Did you ever try to think why your visions have taken the form of cross-bones and snakes?" inquired the doctor in a simple manner.

"And also little white skulls sometimes," added the patient almost inaudibly. She again became silent. Dr. Ford sat looking out of the window where a bright red winter sun had begun to sink above the tops of the hills. Finally she reached for his hand and in a voice low and calm she said:

"I think I can tell you more about it now. It's about Julia, my baby. I never wanted her. I did not want Luther to be her father. I didn't want to marry him fifteen years ago. As years went by I could not stand him—stand the noises he made when he hawked as he cleared his throat. That is a nasty habit of his. I could have screamed when he sniffled. When he sucked his teeth I felt as if a sharp pin were being drawn over my body. I don't think I hate this man—he's not bad—but I can't stand the things he does."

"And you wished him dead."

"And I wished him dead. Oh, Doctor," she moaned, "am I sick or am I just a sinner?" Dr. Ford could see her left leg bend the covers. Mrs. Perry seemed unconscious of it.

"Who am I to judge, Mrs. Perry," said Ford quietly as he intuitively decided that the moment had come for him to bring some of the patient's revelations into association with her symptoms. Often he would make such comments without reasoning out that the proper time had arrived but experience had taught him when he could do so without disturbing the patient's emotional balance too intensely.

Now he continued in his matter of fact, slightly pedantic manner. "Of one thing most of us psychiatrists are sure—that there is no such thing as absolute freedom of the will and that when our instincts clash too hard with our ideals our bodies often pay the penalty. The poets and writers of all lands knew that. Do you know Nathaniel Hawthorne? You may have read *The Scarlet Letter* in high school, Mrs. Perry. The story of the minister's decline in health till he seemed likely to die under the weight of his guilt and responsibility as the father of the child for whom Hester Prynne wore the scarlet A is all written very plainly in that pathetic tale."

"I read it in high school but I don't remember it," replied Mrs. Perry disinterested.

"You mentioned Julia just a little while ago," he pursued.

"Yes, my own baby, Doctor, I must tell you. She has never been Luther's baby in my mind. The more my aversion to Luther grew, the more I became unfaithful to him in my mind. In my crazy imagination I became married to a boy I had fallen in love with at high school. I did not know him well—certainly he did not know I was in love with him. It has all been so foolish, so silly, so insane, yet so awfully real."

"Have you been seeing him lately?"

"Not since I married. His name was Aaron Rubin, a Jewish boy. I think he's a lawyer in Philadelphia now—very successful, I've heard."

"A phantom lover, then?"

"Yes, but in my fancy to me more live than Luther. He gave me all those little attentions which I craved. Then Julia came—an accident. I began to hate her because she was not Aaron's—later to love her because a woman does love a helpless little part of herself. I was never too social—somehow I could not get close to the few women here in the village whom I liked from a distance. My life with Aaron became an obsession. My hatred of Julia grew with my love for her."

Another long silence followed. By now the sun had disappeared and the limbs of the trees on the hills stood out in dark relief against the snow and the cold blue sky. Outside all nature was hushed and the brief twilight of winter had already begun to darken the room. Suddenly Mrs. Perry gave an agonized shriek:

"Oh, doctor, I must tell. One night three years ago

Luther was in his bed beside mine. All evening long he had been hawking. Then he had fallen into a deep sleep—snoring, whistling through his teeth. Loud noises don't bother me only soft, hissing noises which people seem sure to repeat. For hours I had lain awake squirming, he lying there peacefully sleeping beside me. All at once I felt myself turned into a lioness. I felt I must kill Julia. I walked to her bed and had my hands around her little throat ready to choke her. Something happened—my mind spun—my legs gave way. I felt myself collapsing. I dragged myself back to bed. My legs were paralyzed. Oh, Doctor, Doctor, tell me, am I full of sin or am I insane?"

She turned on her side toward him with an imploring look in her wide eyes and clasped her hands in anguish. As she did so she bent her knees under the bedclothes as a person might in prayer.

"I think you will get well, Mrs. Perry," said the doctor as he noted the unconscious movement of her legs. She did not stir again. Ford waited a few minutes. Then he observed, "Look, Mrs. Perry, you have bent your knees."

A minute later Miss Abbie opened the door to the bedroom. "Mrs. Sawtell wants tew talk with yew on the 'phone downstairs," she said dryly and looked maliciously at her sister-in-law.

As Ford passed her he said, "Do you suppose you could get a dressing robe for Mrs. Perry while I'm downstairs, Miss Abbie?"

At the 'phone Mrs. Sawtell's cheery voice said, "For goodness' sake—what in the world has become of you, Dr. Ford. Salty 'phoned from the hospital—he's on his way home—thought you were there hours ago. I know he'll be dead tired when he comes, so can I come out in my car to get you. I'll be there in about half an hour."

"That will be fine. Thanks a lot."

Ford went out on the small front porch. The air had become crisp and much colder—the landscape barely visible was beginning to fade. Yellow windows of light had begun to glow in the houses along the Y and here and there among the black hills. He walked up and down a few minutes, took a few puffs from a cigarette and then returned to the sitting room where he sat for a while smoking. Miss Abbie must have come downstairs while he was on the porch because when he entered her room Mrs. Perry was again alone, a single light emphasizing the thinness of her tense, sad face. She had on a faded blue flannel robe but he could see that she had again extended her legs.

"You know now, Mrs. Perry, that those bad legs of yours will move for you. Let's try if they won't support you. Come, try it. I'll help you to stand. Just put your weight on me. It will take you a little while to do it and be sure of yourself. That's it," he said encouragingly.

She stood uncertainly, then took two feeble steps forward. The doctor helped her back to bed. He sat on the chair in the dim light of the room waiting for a long time.

"Can you stand more light now?" he asked as he sought the switch of the ceiling fixture and turned it on. The light blinded them both for several seconds. Then Mrs. Perry looked at him, weeping a little and said,

"I am convinced that I will walk."

"I had intended going back to New York on the night train but now I have decided to stay over and will be back to see you tomorrow morning. I want to get you started a little more surely on your path. I guess that's the car coming up the hill for me now. Take Dr. Sawtell's sleeping tablets as usual. Good-night, Mrs. Perry, I hope you sleep well."

"Thank you, Doctor."

Miss Abbie did not leave the kitchen to talk with Dr. Ford when he came down but satisfied the amenities by calling out coldly, "Going now?"

Mrs. Sawtell was waiting for him at the front door in an

old Studebaker open car, bundled in a heavy ulster, her cheeks glowing red, her eyes sparkling with health.

"So there you are, I had visions of you eloping with that attractive Mrs. Perry—then I remembered that fortunately she cannot walk—so that explanation vanished. What could you have been doing there all this time?"

"Just talking with her—it's an interesting case."

Mrs. Sawtell looked politely sceptical.

"She must be fascinating. You conscientious doctors are all the same—an interesting case and you forget the world outside exists. Only about two months ago Salty sat up the live-long night with a case of pneumonia during the crisis—one of the prettiest young women in our set and she had one of the prettiest nurses who ever graduated from the Binghamton Hospital. Did you do anything for your patient besides entertaining her?" asked Mrs. Sawtell doubtfully.

"I have great hope that she will walk again. Salty's diagnosis is correct."

"Well, I'm sure that he will be happy about that. We'll celebrate with a good steak tonight and there'll be plenty of time for you two to chin together before you catch your night train."

"You're not getting rid of me so soon. May I stay 'til tomorrow? I want to see Mrs. Perry again."

"That's grand—after supper we can go to see Mary Pickford—she's at the Lyceum and the line will be a block long. But the manager is a patient of Salty's and he lets us in by the side door if we 'phone. Salty is daffy about Mary Pickford and so am I. Let's all be frivolous tonight."

The next morning Mrs. Sawtell and Salty ran Dr. Ford over to Hesta. Gert had induced Salty to go to church that morning just so the entire year would not slip by without a single appearance. They warned Ford to be ready to come back from the Perrys by the time they returned from services in an hour or so.

Mrs. Perry looked rested and refreshed. She said that her stomach had stopped churning and she had spent most of the time that morning testing her ankles and knees to make sure that they actually worked.

"Did Dr. Sawtell say anything about Julia," she then inquired apprehensively.

"He expects that her leg will be as good as ever. The x-rays show that the break has been set perfectly."

"Thank God," murmured Mrs. Perry.

"And now let's test your own legs again."

Mrs. Perry stood unsteadily, then with Dr. Ford's help tottered from the side to the foot of the bed where she turned and stood alone holding on to the white dresser. At first she seemed amazed at her own accomplishment—then began to weep softly and continued to weep as the doctor helped her to the chair beside the bed. Soon she managed to take the few steps back to bed where she sat as if dazed.

"What has happened to me, Doctor?" she stammered mystified. "What have you done for me? I never thought I would walk again."

"All I can say is that sometimes our minds find odd, almost inscrutable ways of protecting us from catastrophes or from tasks which appear unsurmountable to us just at a particular time. Could it be in your case that your legs not functioning saved you from harming Julia, whom I know you love very dearly—far more, I think, than your own happiness?"

"I think I see," she murmured as tears appeared again. "You mean I became helpless so that I would be unable to choke my little girl."

"Yes, just exactly that. And maybe you stayed helpless so that should the temptation ever come back you would not be able to make the attempt again. I would say that you were so uncertain as to what the violent impulses might do that your better self unconsciously took good care they should not get the upper hand of you."

A fleeting smile of appreciation which passed over the patient's face told Ford that she had grasped the idea.

"I must tell you something, Doctor. Yesterday when you went down to answer Mrs. Sawtell's 'phone, I prayed to Jesus. I have never been a regular church-goer and during the years before I became sick I never went much. For many months while I was lying here alone in bed my thoughts never ceased dwelling on my guilt about Aaron and Luther and Julia and about numerous, long forgotten feelings inside me. I blamed myself but it was not possible to talk about them. But last night again I prayed and prayed with all my heart to Jesus—I know now that God will help me to walk."

"Yes, your faith will certainly help hasten the cure."

"But something else happened. As I lay there last night my thoughts went back to early happenings—all sorts of old things. In the house across the way from ours lived a lone, elderly widow. On pleasant, sunny Sunday afternoons she would sit in a rocking chair on her front porch singing hymns to herself—but one hymn she kept singing over and over again—it went something like this: 'Throw out the life-line, throw out the life-line, some one is drifting away; throw out the life-line, some one is sinking today'. And then I thought of me sinking, almost drowning, and you, Doctor, coming to save me just at the right time."

"Be that as it may," said Dr. Ford, "I think that you will be walking into the hospital to see Julia before she is able to come home to you. Let's try walking once again before I leave—just to make doubly sure that the connection between your head and your feet has grown stronger through your exercises."

"And maybe soon I can get around to do my own housework—and maybe help Luther at the stome—he's been so hard pressed."

"Perhaps that will come about sooner than you expect. Sometimes these things go quite fast when the tide once turns and the flow is reversed from illness to health. You know there is no damage done to a telephone wire if no messages go over it for a while. The nerves from your brain to your feet are ready to carry messages as soon as your mind starts giving them. Soon now you will find your legs responding naturally."

"I never knew such a thing could happen," whispered Mrs. Perry as if to herself.

"But doctors have known these things for a long time," persisted Ford to drive home the concept of the power of mental influence. "Only of late years they have not given too much attention to them because all the new scientific discoveries in surgery and antitoxins and all the marvelous new drugs have interested them more."

"When are you going back to New York?"

"This afternoon—but Dr. Sawtell will come up to see you or talk with you over the 'phone when you go downstairs. We'll have one last try at standing. That's fine—practice by yourself—Miss Abbie will be surprised."

"And maybe she'll get out soon," added Mrs. Perry with a display of new spirit which seemed encouraging to the doctor.

Mrs. Sawtell came alone to call for Ford in the battered, open runabout. She appeared impatient, started the car a bit abruptly and explained that even at church Salty had been given no peace—an anxious father had been waiting for him as he came out and persuaded him to see his child— temperature 104—three miles out in the country.

"Jiminy Crickets, you didn't spend all that time again this morning talking with that woman," remarked Mrs. Sawtell with a touch of impatience as she swung into the

main road and shifted quickly into high. She now appeared
suspicious of the whole procedure at the little house on the
hill.

"Can you really accomplish anything that way, Dr. Ford?
Oh, I suppose yes—Salty says so—but I'm glad he's sticking
to pills and plasters and surgery. Oh, I suppose I shouldn't
have said that—but I'm outspoken—never could hold my
tongue when I know I'm right. Oh, golly, I guess I'd better
keep quiet this minute."

"That's all right. I'm not offended. I've heard that often,
ever so often before—not only from folks like you who don't
know me but from my favorite aunt who regards me as a
sort of high-toned quack. Quite a few of my doctor friends,
who should know better, are the bitterest scoffers. It got
back to me recently from a patient whom one of them had
actually sent to me. He is a laboratory man who cuts up hun-
dreds of dogs and cats and whom the anti-vivisectionists are
after hot and heavy. The patient told me after a time that
Doctor X said that I was keen all right—a good man—but
crazy as a bedbug with that psychoanalytic twaddle. So you
see, Mrs. Sawtell, I can surely understand how you feel about
it and that's quite all right."

Mrs. Sawtell gave Ford an incredulous look but also a
smile which seemed to express appreciation not of what Dr.
Ford had said but that he had taken no offense at her disapproval.

Salty got back from his call late and while driving Ford to
the station they talked over the generalities of what had
happened with Mrs. Perry and that she had actually gotten
out of bed. When they reached the platform, Ford said:

"I think it will be best if I do not tell even you the
details of Mrs. Perry's story. She prefers to keep it to herself.
Let her continue to take her pills for sleeping. Visit her in
a few days, instruct her to try new uses of her legs—going
downstairs, kneeling, standing on one leg and the like. I feel

almost sure she will be walking quite well in a week or two.
Of course, your diagnosis has been the right one—hysteria,
a conversion hysteria to be more exact, with some mental
manifestations for which we psychiatrists have our unintelligible jargon. You don't mind my not going into particulars
just now, Salty, do you? Let me hear how she comes out, and
thank you for asking me to come."

"You'll hear from me. Goodbye, Dr. Ford, and thanks for
your help."

Dr. Ford returned to the records of the case. His secretary
at that time had been Miss Moore, a meticulous, elderly lady.
Punctilliously attached were two letters—one from Dr. Sawtell in a scrawly, spreading script, and the other a carbon
copy of his own reply.

"Binghamton, January 26, 1920

My dear Dr. Ford:

*I have been wanting to write you since the first of
the year about the Perry case but something always
interfered. I was rushed to death with a flu epidemic
which is on the wane, and to cap it all Peppy came down
with measles. Gert, who expects an addition to the
family in about six months has been quite miserable.
Both are about well, now, so here goes.*

*Mrs. Perry went down to the hospital to see Julia
about a week ago. We will still have Julia's leg in
traction for a few days. I had very little to do with
Mrs. Perry's recovery—talked with her pretty near
every night over the 'phone but saw her only once—
about a week after you left. She was already moving
about the house for several hours a day and Miss Abbie
had gone home. I guess that suited Luther as well as
Mrs. Perry.*

Of course the whole village of Hesta is divided in its opinion in regard to the cure of Mrs. Perry. All sorts of gossip and conjecture went around but the majority agreed with Miss Abbie that 'there never war anything much the matter with her anyhow'. On the other hand, some have regarded it as a mild miracle. Gert has been perplexed—doesn't 'understand it at all', but told me to be sure to write you that she hoped you did not think her rude.

All I can say is that Mrs. Perry has been down to Binghamton three times now and has been at Luther's store helping him in the late afternoon. He cannot quite comprehend the whole thing but I have a hunch she is treating him better than she used to. And I must say that I don't know exactly what happened to Mrs. Perry or why or how it happened since you told me only that my diagnosis was right. And I know there must be a good reason so we'll let it go at that.

Hoping you will drop in to see us if you ever pass this way, I am

Yours faithfully,

Thomas (Salty) Sawtell."

Then Dr. Ford read over his reply.

"New York, February 10, 1920

Dr. Thomas Sawtell
121 Park Street
Binghampton
New York

My dear Salty:

I wish to thank you for your letter and gratifying report on Mrs. Perry. I am very happy to know that she is recovered and has stayed so for some weeks.

I do feel that I owe you an apology for not having given you more details of what happened. I hope you will understand—maybe some time when the case is ancient history I'll have the privilege of telling you the origin of the illness. All I can say now is that the paralysis was a protective symptom against certain dangerous impulses, an explanation which I must admit cannot be satisfactory to you. I need hardly add that the symptoms developed involuntarily and were beyond the control of Mrs. Perry.

Now as for the 'cure'. During our talks, Mrs. Perry told me some very personal things which we reviewed at length. We must have spent five hours at it and she did most of the talking after she finally got started. The Catholic clergy and many other people beside them know that the confessional unburdening to another individual is good for the soul. It has been known for centuries that the body often must suffer under the stress of mental conflicts and secrets scrupulously guarded.

Of course, I explained to Mrs. Perry how the mind quite unconsciously takes intricate ways like hers to achieve compromises which serve their function but which are rarely fully satisfactory. I was able also to alleviate her fear of insanity which had greatly terrified her because I could speak on this topic with assurance and authority. I pointed out to her that her difficulties could be met in healthier ways and that these paths were open and beckoning to her.

I have gradually come to appreciate that in psychic cures it is not only who the physician is and what the physician says to a patient but that equally important is the time at which he says it. And here is where unusual luck was with us all. You may have suspected that certain difficulties in the Perry household were

*upsetting the patient and that these also involved Julia.
The accident to Julia thus became opportune for fur-
thering the cure. When certain hostile feelings which
Mrs. Perry had toward Julia were exposed in our talks,
strong emotions of love and responsibility surged
and replaced them. Unconsciously the need to walk so
as to see her child overcame the former need to stay
paralyzed. This is the only way in which I can account
for the extraordinarily rapid success of my talks with
her. I believe that had I come at another time it might
have taken weeks or months to accomplish the same
results.*

*With best wishes and thanks to Gert and you for
your hospitality, I am*

Yours cordially,

Benjamin Ford."

As Dr. Ford finished reading his reply written twenty odd
years before, it astonished him how little some of those be-
liefs about the cure of neuroses had changed with all the
varied experiences in the intervening time. Then he reflected that most of the essential ideas of Freud had been well
formulated before the first World War and that their application in treatment was an art rather than a science; that
success or failure sometimes depended upon many ex-
traneous factors as well as the skill and patience of the physician in unraveling deeply seated conflicts.

Ford picked up the artless Christmas card of Julia Perry's
little son. Twenty-five cards had preceded it. He remembered
his keen pleasure when he had received the first one at the
Christmas following his visit to the village on the Susquehanna. Little Julia Perry—his "frend"—had drawn a small
red house with smoke curling up from a chimney against a

pale blue sky. She had pasted a crescent moon and a star cut from silver foil over the top of the house. From her a card had come each year—hand made, and each year more skillfully designed as the girl grew up. Each contained a simple note from Mrs. Perry of the little family's doings and progress—Luther's success as manager of a chain store in Elmira, Mrs. Perry's activity in women's work at the Presbyterian Church, Julia's graduation with "honors in art" from high school, her marriage to a "very nice boy named Homer Brown", her motherhood and now the child-like card from her little son Perry—Dr. Ford's new, unknown "frend". Together the cards had told a homely story of the struggle and growth and development of the humble family.

"Yes", mused the doctor with a warm feeling of contentment as he leaned back heavily in his swivel chair, put his feet on his desk and gazed at the rings of smoke which he blew slowly from his cigar. "Little, yellow-haired Perry Brown had done well when he chose to draw a tall, green Christmas tree on the card for his 'frend'."

Ford got up with some effort from his worn desk chair to replace the file box on the dusty shelf from which he had taken it. The chimes from the Metropolitan Tower rang out in low tones, striking the four quarters and then eleven full, deep notes. He walked slowly to the window of his waiting room and gazed out over the leafless trees of the deserted park in the square. Then he turned and sank heavily into the deep, frayed arm-chair. He felt his joints creak a bit. He might not be there, he thought, to reecive many more cards from Perry Brown. Once the aunt of a patient whom he had cured remarked to him: "You psychiatrists at times seem to work miracles—but that is no reason for us to expect that you should do it all the time."

A long series of cases passed fleetingly through the doctor's mind; the fifty-five year old manufacturer whom he had liberated from the tyranny of his eighty year old father, the young Italian girl, moribund from colitis who blossomed out into vigorous health. He remembered too the guileless thirteen year old girl whose pregnancy was discovered in the fifth month and whom with her family he had enabled to meet the situation. Of course, there had been some discouraging outcomes, as with poor Rosalie Stein, where he had felt the sting of defeat. But Ford was content. There were enough happy results in his memory, like the Perrys, to make him feel that way.